The Many Faces of MAID

What to Expect When

Someone You Know

Chooses Medical Assistance in Dying

Cynthia Clark & Carol Cram

MAID FAMILY SUPPORT SOCIETY
info@maidfamilysupport.ca
604.723.2400
www.maidfamilysupport.ca

ISBN: 978-1-7380516-2-5

Cover Design: John Dowler, www.cosmicidea.com
Cover Art: *Paths of Light,* acrylic on canvas, by Gregg Simpson
www.greggsimpsonart.com

Printed and bound in Canada

All proceeds from sales of this book are going directly to the MAID Family Support Society (www.maidfamilysupport.ca) to assist them with their work with families impacted by MAID.

SUPPORT FOR THE MANY FACES OF MAID

In the simplest sense, this book is an important read. There is a dearth of MAID grief-related resources, and these stories are needed, will be valued, and can act as navigation tools for those considering medical assistance in dying as well as those supporting them. I regularly listen to people wondering if it's better to let their "wounds close", and I ask them to trust that wanting to know more about their grief is healing and healthy.
- Keri-Lyn Durant, PhD, Heartsteps Centre for Grief Literacy

The Many Faces of MAID is a welcome addition to the resources available for people supporting, or who have supported, someone having MAID. In our experiences at MAiDHouse, we have found that stories about MAID are very powerful, whether from the person having MAID, or from friends, families and others who are supporting them, or from the professionals who ensure access to our legislative right. *The Many Faces of MAID* is a grief support group on a page. It provides an opportunity for the storytellers to generously share their experiences and a perfect place for readers to find support through shared but also unique experiences.
-Tekla Hendrickson, Executive Director, MAiDHouse

I would have buried myself in these writings if this were available at the time. Can't wait until it's out and I can share with my circle. I am positive it will be a beautiful resource for many, many more folks to come.
-Shannon Knight, Registered Respiratory Therapist and one of the storytellers who participated in the writing of The Many Faces of MAID

The Many Faces of MAID is an invaluable touchstone for anyone experiencing the grief of a loved one's medically assisted death - its frank storytelling, from multiple viewpoints, is a tender reminder that you are not alone.
-Sheryl Williamson, End of Life Doula - Mindful Mortality

The Many Faces of MAID encapsulates so beautifully the experiences of those who navigate the waves of the assisted dying process — before, during and after. This compilation of stories honours grief, love and loss in their purest form and allows readers the opportunity to step into the lives of the storytellers in their own way. Resources like this are vital and we at Bridge C-14 are proud supporters of this work. Let's keep the conversation going.
- Lauren Clark, President & CEO, Bridge C-14

DEDICATION

This book is dedicated to my children and to anyone who has ever struggled with talking about hard feelings. Your resilience, openness and empathy surprise me every day. I never wanted your father's death to be the event that ruined your lives, but I didn't imagine it would be what shaped you into the profoundly wonderful humans that you have become.
"Just because it's not easy doesn't mean it's not worth it."

Cynthia Clark

For my mother—my cheerleader, my support, my everything—who in choosing how she wanted to die taught me why to live.

Carol Cram

IN MEMORIAM

To all our loved ones who, in leaving us,
inspired us to be part of this book.

George Ballard

Gary Berger

Horacio Bouzas

Wendy Bowen

Scott Chinnery

Gary Clark

Ruby Cram

Sharon Douglas

Annie Dugan

Ralph Ethier

Valerie Ethier

Mike Hounslow

Zaki Mabro

Duncan McLean

Anna Milton

Kimberly O'Brien

Bob Putnam

Veronica Shirey

CONTENTS

CONTENTS

FOREWORD

My dad had a medically assisted death (MAID) in 2018, just two years after it was legalized in Canada. It was such a gift that he could die with dignity on his own terms. I have been a nurse for 35 years, and intimately familiar with death, so I thought I knew what to expect and what was coming. Although at the time I wasn't looking for support, now thinking back, I wish I'd had the option to speak with someone with lived experience, who understood the anguish, the ticking clock, and the sadness, and who could help to validate my feelings or just be there to listen.

My Dad's final words were to the physician, to "keep doing the amazing work you are doing with MAID." This comment stayed with me and so I started researching what resources existed for families in Canada only to discover there were few to none.

In 2021, I was finally able to honour my dad's wishes by launching the MAID Family Support Society (MFSS). We are a group of volunteers who have been through MAID with a loved one. We provide compassionate, peer-to-peer support to others helping a loved one who is considering or planning for MAID, or who is grieving a loss following MAID. Our volunteer group is growing and is the heart and soul of our organization.

Through my work with MAID Family Support Society, I frequently witness how stories help people feel less alone. I think we are drawn to stories that help us make sense of our lived experience and confirm that what we are feeling or going through is normal or common.

For many of us who have supported a loved one along the MAID journey, just knowing that others can personally relate to what we're going through is a comfort. We need to hear these stories in a way that resonates with us, whether it's over the phone, on a video or via the written word as it is in *The Many Faces of MAID*.

The stories in this book offer us real, emotional connections to the raw and uncensored experiences of a medically assisted death. I believe this book will be a valuable resource for the MAID community. It aligns perfectly with the work of MFSS by reassuring readers that whatever they are feeling at any given moment is okay.

There is no right or wrong way to feel about our loved one's MAID death. I encourage readers to jump into this book at any point that reflects where they are on the MAID journey and to know that they are not alone.

I think my dad would be so proud of the work that MAID Family Support Society is doing, and he would be happy this book is available to support the community of loved ones experiencing MAID.

I am deeply grateful to Carol and Cynthia for their amazing work, bringing these important stories to print and for gifting the proceeds from all sales of *The Many Faces of MAID* to the MAID Family Support Society.

And finally, a big thank you to the storytellers who shared such an intimate and precious time in their lives. Your courage is an inspiration.

Signy Novak
Founder of MAID Family Support Society
www.maidfamilysupport.ca

INTRODUCTION

The Many Faces of MAID is a compilation of stories from seventeen people who have direct experience of their loved one choosing a medically assisted death. Think of this book as a grief support group on a page. If you've helped or watched a loved one, a family member or a friend access Medical Assistance in Dying (MAID), this book will be the support group you didn't know you needed. Maybe it can accompany you on your own unique journey to help you cope with the sad, confusing, despairing, joyous, hopeless, and tender realities of your loved one having a medically assisted death.

The purpose of *The Many Faces of MAID* is to validate the myriad of emotions you may feel before, during, and after someone in your life has chosen and is approved for a medically assisted death. This book is *not* about how MAID works or a guide on 'how to have a dignified death' or a comprehensive explanation of the Canadian MAID legislation.

In *The Many Faces of MAID*, you'll find stories that encompass a wide range of emotions, from easy to difficult and from expected to unexpected. Our storytellers are real, and their emotions are raw and honest. The perspectives they offer are not complete accounts of their experiences. Rather, they are small glimpses into some of the intimate moments and emotions they've felt moved to share with others.

This book provides you with opportunities to find comfort, companionship, and validation of your own emotions. It's also a chance for you to explore the many feelings you are likely to experience before, during, and after your loved one's medically assisted death. You may experience many of the emotions expressed in these pages, or you may experience different emotions. Every journey is unique, and every journey is valid.

YOU SHOULD READ THIS BOOK IF...

- You are a son, daughter, spouse, caregiver, parent, sibling, friend, or cousin of a person who has chosen or might choose a medically assisted death.
- You fully supported, had mixed emotions about, or disagreed with your loved one's diagnosis and their end-of-life choices.
- You are seeking to process your own feelings before and/or after a planned death.
- You are an observer, teacher, clergy member, medical provider, volunteer, doula, or co-worker who wishes to support a person directly affected by MAID.
- You are an acquaintance or neighbour who is surprised by the range of emotions you felt after learning about a medically assisted death.
- You want to gain a deeper understanding of the emotions felt by anyone touched by MAID.

No matter who you are and what your relationship is to MAID, use this book to help you understand that at any point in the MAID journey, your feelings are valid, and you are not alone.

Introduction

HOW TO READ THIS BOOK

The Many Faces of MAID is a resource you can dip into as your moods and needs shift from day to day and month to month. You don't need to read this book from cover to cover—and you probably shouldn't! Think of the book as a companion that you can reference to validate whatever emotions you are feeling at a particular time. There is no right or wrong way to experience *The Many Faces of MAID*.

You might start by reading the descriptions of the storytellers to find someone you can relate to, perhaps someone whose loved one had a similar diagnosis to that experienced by your loved one, or someone whose relationship to their loved one is the same as yours.

You might then page through the book to read about how their experience at various stages of the MAID journey may or may not resemble your own. Alternatively, you may start with the chapter that most closely represents where you are chronologically on your own journey with MAID.

You may well discover that the person whom you thought most resembled you when you started reading does not always share feelings or reactions that you can relate to. You may find validation of your feelings from unexpected storytellers at unexpected times. It's important to note that while each storyteller only presents one emotion per chapter, most of us could have told an anecdote about a time we felt any and all of the emotions presented. We've tried to highlight the emotions we expected to feel, as well as the ones that surprised us, challenged us, and felt difficult to grapple with.

Introduction

We suggest you read this book with a pen and paper handy and to use the prompts provided to reflect on and write about your own feelings and experiences.

HOW THIS BOOK IS ORGANIZED

The Many Faces of MAID is organized into chapters. In Chapter 1, our storytellers share their feelings and attitudes about death and dying. For many, the MAID death of their loved one was the first time they've had to confront death head on.

Chapters 2 through 9 are organized into eight stages of the MAID journey.

- Chapter 2: Diagnosis: Beginning of the End
- Chapter 3: Discovering MAID
- Chapter 4: Getting Approved for MAID
- Chapter 5: Saying Goodbye
- Chapter 6: MAID Day
- Chapter 7: After MAID
- Chapter 8: Finding Support after MAID
- Chapter 9: Moving Forward

At each of these stages, our storytellers describe their experience of one emotion, such as hope, confusion, resentment, anxiety, joy, or love. No emotion is off the table in *The Many Faces of MAID*.

At the end of this book, you'll find an index of emotions and a comprehensive list of MAID resources at both the national and provincial levels.

Our intention is for you to find support for a wide range of emotions at various times in your own journey. For example, you may feel angry on a day when you're helping your loved one navigate the system to procure MAID. Pick up *The Many Faces of MAID* and see if one of the storytellers also felt angry during that

Introduction

stage. Reading about their experience may help you process your own experience and support your emotions.

Or maybe, while saying goodbye to your loved one, you feel an overwhelming love for them. In the chapter on Saying Goodbye, see if one of our storytellers wrote about love.

If a story or an emotion doesn't resonate with you on a particular day, skip it and find one that does. If you are feeling an emotion that isn't included in a particular chapter, look for that emotion in other chapters or from other storytellers. Also, consider using the prompts provided to write about your own feelings. No emotion is off the table.

NOTES ABOUT THE WRITING PROCESS

The Many Faces of MAID was compiled by Cynthia Clark and Carol Cram, who were both closely involved with the MAID death of their loved one. They discovered a shared passion for writing and for helping others navigate the MAID experience.

When they first met to discuss MAID and writing a book, they realized they each brought unique but complementary skills and ideas to the table. Cynthia envisioned coaching groups of people to write their own stories and move towards healing, and Carol imagined a compilation of stories to help support others in the future.

After circulating an initial request for interested participants, Cynthia and Carol described the time commitment and process to approximately 30 interested individuals. Over a period of eight months, seventeen individuals committed to and participated in meetings, writing workshops, and editing sessions to produce *The Many Faces of MAID*. Each storyteller had full control over the words they included in this book and agreed to have them shared.

Introduction

No one was turned away from participating in this project, and every effort was made to include diverse perspectives and voices from across Canada.

WORD CHOICES

Throughout the writing process, we spent a lot of time thinking about the specific words we wanted to use when referring to our contributors and the people they supported.

We know that not everyone who reads this book will feel represented by all the terminology we've chosen, and we would be sorry if our language choices turned people away from a resource that could provide great comfort. Producing a book that is considerate to each reader's needs, while also accurately representing our own lived experiences has been a delicate balancing exercise. Two terms in particular received reactions from early reviewers and sparked discussions that we feel warrant an explanation:

- **Storyteller**: how we refer to ourselves
- **Loved One**: how we refer to the person we supported through MAID.

How We Refer to Ourselves (Storyteller)

The term, 'participants' felt too impersonal for people who were publicly sharing such intimate moments of their lives, and 'writers' created a lot of pressure for all of us to be skilled at putting our feelings into words.

In early drafts, we used the term 'survivors' because we had all 'survived' the experience of someone in our lives dying with MAID. However, we soon realized that 'survivor' might be triggering to people who are struggling in their journey or who are feeling conflicted or unsupportive of MAID. The term

Introduction

'survivor' could also confuse people with less knowledge of MAID, perhaps implying that MAID itself might end in survival (life), instead of death.

We decided that the term 'storytellers' best resonates with our intention for *The Faces of MAID*, which is to share our personal experiences as people who have supported someone else having MAID.

How We Refer to Our Person (Loved One)

Our storytellers generally felt that the term 'our person' was too impersonal and clinical because each of us were very closely connected to our 'loved one'. However, we understand that not everyone who reads this book will feel that their connection to MAID is with a 'loved one'.

In keeping with the feelings of the storytellers in this book, we've decided to use the term 'loved one' most of the time, and only occasionally use the term 'your person'. Our sense is that if you've come to seek validation for your feelings during a MAID event, even complicated grievers probably lost a 'loved one' even if you didn't/don't feel love for them.

THIS IS *NOT* A SELF HELP BOOK

Our purpose in writing *The Many Faces of MAID* is to present the experiences and emotions of our storytellers in the hope that readers find validation and comfort from peers. We are not therapists, and while this book may offer therapeutic benefit, it is not a substitute for therapy.

We provide prompts in the 'How Do You Feel?' boxes throughout the book in an effort to keep readers focused on their own feelings. Our stories are examples of how one person felt, but they are not prescriptions for how a reader should feel. It is not our intention to push readers to analyze, challenge or change the way they feel.

We've purposely created a resource that offers peer validation as opposed to a book designed to help people process or analyze grief.

Cynthia Clark & Carol Cram

MEET THE STORYTELLERS

Our storytellers are all people who have lived through the medically assisted death of a loved one in Canada. Some are spouses and children; others are close friends. Some were supporters or even advocates of the MAID decision, while others were not involved in the process, or struggled with their loved one's choice to have MAID.

The only unifying factor is that each of our storytellers has been directly impacted by someone else's decision to have MAID. In order to process their emotions, they've chosen to share their experiences with others.

Following is a short description of each of the storytellers who contributed to *The Many Faces of MAID* organized according to their relationship to their loved one — spouse, child, parent, or friend. In this and all subsequent chapters, both Cynthia and Carol, the compilers of this book, share their stories about the MAID deaths of their loved one.

SPOUSES

Jane

My husband was diagnosed with pulmonary fibrosis in his late 70's. As his lungs deteriorated, he spoke of ending his life before he needed to be on a respirator. He decided he wanted to have MAID three years after his diagnosis, but suffered another two

11

years before deciding he was ready. I struggled with his decision initially, as my grandson had recently completed suicide and I didn't know how I would cope with both deaths so close together. I also had to reconcile with my faith community's acceptance of MAID. The two years following his initial decision was an emotional rollercoaster because he kept saying yes, I'm ready then, no I'm not. When finally, my husband's daily existence became intolerable, he chose to die peacefully, with those he loved by his side.

Dave L.

Annie and I were both in our late 70's and had been living with Annie's condition and its inevitable conclusion for almost 30 years. Neither of us feared death, and Annie had always been clear that once her pain and suffering started to become unmanageable, she would end her life by whatever means were available. MAID removed all uncertainty and transformed death into a profound journey filled with love and joy and laughter.

Cathy

Gary and I were in our 70s and had been together for 28 years when he was diagnosed with mesothelioma, an incurable lung cancer. What followed was Gary's gradual decline over the next year and a half, with me taking care of him. We agreed from the beginning that neither of us could tolerate his prolonged suffering and that MAID was the right choice. Gary decided to forgo treatment that might extend his life for a few months but would affect the quality of the time he had left. He died peacefully at home, overlooking the beauty of the lake behind our house.

Bobbie

Bob and I had been married for 28 active and healthy years when he was diagnosed with Parkinson's Disease. We lived our lives to the fullest for another 23 years. After an isolating and demoralizing five-week stay in the hospital during COVID, Bob decided he wanted to go home and die on his own terms. I was with him, and our dog was by his side, as he looked out into our garden and said goodbye.

Dave B.

Annie and I had lived on a street aptly named Paradise Close for three blissful years when Annie, at 72, was diagnosed with Stage 4 colon cancer. At the same time, she lost her speech and her ability to eat, a condition that was strongly suspected to be Bulbar ALS. She became palliative right away. A hospice visitor told us about MAID, and the relief for both of us was palpable. We smiled at each other, knowing that Annie would not have to die in pain.

I was her primary caregiver for 20 months, a role I never wanted, but gratefully embraced. She managed the cancer, but a much deeper blow was her inability to talk to me. We'd been together, as the tightest unit imaginable, for 27 years when Annie decided she'd had enough. She had the most beautiful, peaceful death on our living room sofa in the presence of her two children and me, her loving husband.

Geneviève

I was 54 when my husband was diagnosed with early onset Alzheimer's. He would have been ill and on the decline for many decades to come had he not decided even before he was diagnosed that he wanted to do MAID. He went to the hospital to have MAID so that he could donate his organs. Our two children and I were by his side.

Emily

I met Veronica, the love of my life, when I was 21 years old. We'd been together for 18 years when she was first diagnosed with breast cancer. For a year, I went to all of her medical appointments and gave her as much love and support as I could. We rejoiced when she was told she was cancer free. But even though Veronica went back to daily living, she never felt like herself. The chemotherapy did damage to her mind, body and spirit, but she pushed forward as best she could.

Veronica's life turned for the worse when she received the devastating news that her cancer had come back and with a vengeance. She had chemotherapy again, but it didn't work. She tried to hide the pain she was in, but I could see it. Veronica was getting tired, and she made the decision to have MAID.

Within a week, Veronica's procedure happened in the comfort of our home with Veronica's children and me beside her as she peacefully closed her eyes forever.

Cynthia

I had just turned 40 and had two young kids, when my husband was diagnosed with terminal brain cancer (glioblastoma). Everything had been totally fine less than four weeks earlier. My husband decided he would do the standard course of treatment and then 'quit while it was still fun' (have MAID), which I wholeheartedly supported. We spoke openly about this decision from the beginning. He received treatment for nine months until his cancer stopped responding to the chemotherapy. One month later, he chose a peaceful death at home, before losing his mobility or ability to live at home.

CHILDREN

Brittney

I was in my mid-20's, living a relatively normal and quiet life when my mother was diagnosed with skin cancer in her jaw. My mom had decided on MAID before going into her first surgery, 'just in case things got bad.' After six years and numerous surgeries, appointments and treatments, the cancer returned for the third time and there was nothing more the doctors could do. Even though she couldn't speak, she made it clear that she was ready to move on to the other side, experience the next chapter, and more importantly, be pain free.

Daimhin

I was in my third year of university when my dad found a lump in his neck while taking a shower. He was diagnosed with an Ewing Sarcoma and underwent chemotherapy, radiation and surgery. He did not want to let the cancer take him, as he had watched happen to his own father, so knew he wanted MAID when the time came. He had a large party to say goodbye to dear friends and family and then he died peacefully at home, past the point he ever wanted to get to, surrounded by his loved ones.

Nikki

I was my father's primary caretaker for well over seven years while raising my two young children and surviving my own bout of cancer. My dad was a dedicated alcoholic whose vision, general health and well-being were declining rapidly when he decided to explore the option of MAID. I acted as his advocate and supported him throughout his journey to receive MAID, which he so desperately wanted. I am fiercely proud of my role in his life and of my father's bravery. He died in the dignified way he desired in the comfort of his home and surrounded by those he loved best.

Robin

I was 46 when my dad chose MAID. He had been sick with interstitial lung disease and had rapidly declined over the course of a year, but his decision to go ahead with MAID still came as a bit of a surprise. He had mentioned the idea over the previous months, but when it came time, he made the decision to proceed with a week's notice. It felt sudden, but it did give us a chance to spend time together and I was able to take my two young kids to say goodbye to their grandpa. My dad died in a care home with four of his kids by his side and another joining by Zoom from Australia. It was a peaceful death on his own terms and timeline.

Elizabeth

I was in my late forties when my mother was diagnosed with cancer, and my fifties when my father was also diagnosed with a different form of cancer. Both of my parents were strong independent people who felt that MAID gave them the choice to end their lives on their own terms and timing. In 2016, my mother used MAID after all cancer treatments had run their course. My father used MAID in 2021 after having suffered mobility issues and chronic pain for many years. Both my mother and father had peaceful deaths in their home with their adult children present.

Carol

Shortly after my 93-year-old mother moved into full-time, long-term care, she decided to 'do MAID.' Although suffering from acute anxiety, limited mobility, and failing health, she was clear-headed and determined, and once she was approved for MAID, she never wavered. As her only child (my brother had already passed), it was up to me to make sure she got what she wanted. On her last day, she was surrounded by her beloved family including her new great-granddaughter. Pictures from that day show her smiling and at peace. She died serenely with me at her side.

Meet the Storytellers

PARENT

Andrée

My daughter Kimberly was my first-born. She was loving, fiercely independent and an artist at heart. At the age of 20, she was diagnosed with cutaneous t-cell lymphoma ('CTCL'). We were told CTCL was an 'old man's disease,' not typically found in young people, and not an aggressive cancer. Sadly, three years later, it became aggressive. I was her main caregiver as she went through seven years of chemotherapy, radiation treatments, and a stem cell transplant. She lived life to the fullest through it all, but when she was told there were no more treatment options, she chose MAID. Kimberly died peacefully in hospital at the age of 31 surrounded by her husband, her sister and me.

FRIENDS

Shannon

I met Wendy in 2013 after moving to Vancouver Island. Our shared love for sport, outdoor adventures and travel cultivated a brilliant friendship. When Wendy was diagnosed with a terminal illness in early 2020, her wild determination and optimism did not falter, but from the very beginning, she was prepared to have MAID as an option in her back pocket. She declined mainstream medical treatments in favour of a holistic approach which provided her the most comfortable and optimal living despite the growing illness. Wendy died beautifully in her home, surrounded with love in late 2021.

Carole

I was stunned and devastated when my close friend Sue called to say that she desperately and urgently needed my support. Her husband Dan had elected to have MAID, and this was a decision

17

that was inconceivably traumatic for Sue. Dan's facial cancer treatment would be painful and result in such disfigurement that he felt he'd prefer to die with some semblance of dignity. I flew to their home, trying to grasp the complexities of this tragedy, to comfort both of my dear friends at the end of Dan's life.

SUMMARY

You are doing a good thing for yourself by picking up this book. Whether it's to help you during the MAID journey of your loved one, to support others coping with their loved one's death, or to find out more about how MAID affects people you know and love, this book is a great place to explore the many feelings associated with a MAID journey.

For those of us 'left behind,' MAID is not an end but a beginning of experiencing an ever-shifting mix of complicated emotions that can be sad and joyful, overwhelming and hopeful, and isolating and connected. Every day, our feelings shift and change, and we wonder if it's normal to feel so many different things.

We hope you find comfort, support, validation and some peace in this book, as you take it with you on your own MAID journey.

CHAPTER 1 -

FEELINGS ABOUT DEATH AND

DYING

Death is not the opposite of life, but a part of it. —
Haruki Murakami

We began the eight-month process of writing *The Many Faces of MAID* by asking each of our storytellers to explore their early experiences with death. We asked them to share the beliefs and feelings about death and dying that they grew up with and held before becoming involved with their loved one's decision to have MAID. We encouraged our new writers to describe crucial moments and the thoughts that accompanied those events.

Your experience and values about death might impact how you experience and process MAID. Our storytellers were asked to consider the following questions as they wrote their first piece for *The Many Faces of MAID:*

- How did you think of death growing up?
- What were some of your beliefs about death?
- What experiences did you have with death and dying?
- What were your emotions around death?

Chapter 1

Jane

I didn't have much experience with death growing up because we immigrated to Canada when I was young and left behind our extended family. When I was twenty-six, my grandmother died and although I knew she was sick, her death was sudden. She had visited us often, and I was close to her. I was not able to attend the funeral, but on the day she was buried, I woke up to her calling my name. Her death felt very surreal to me, especially not seeing her and not saying goodbye. It felt like she just disappeared. My parents never talked about her death, but I always remember feeling a heaviness about it.

My next experience with death became very real when I worked at a veterinary clinic. I was naturally caring and compassionate, so I became the person called in to comfort the pet owners during or after their pet's death. I would ask them to tell me about their pet and allow them to cry in my company. This job became the training ground for my career and calling as a hospital chaplain.

When I decided to become ordained as a deacon in the Anglican Church, part of the training was four months of clinical work in a hospital. In those months, I came to learn that some things were worse than death, which completely changed my understanding of suffering, healing, and death. Of course, I continued to pray with and for people, but I found myself often praying for someone's death as I worked with families as they made tough decisions to remove their loved one from life support.

I went on to work in a hospital setting for twenty years. During this time, I came in contact with many patients begging to be released from their pain and suffering, and all I could do was be present. Around the end of my career, talk of MAID was gaining support. My denomination was not supportive at this time and my opinion was conflicted. We were not allowed to minister to MAID patients or their families or be present at MAID procedures. It seemed cruel to me to ignore everyone's pain, and it became more difficult for me to remain on the outside of this issue. Eventually, our leaders realized their constraints were not compassionate, and we are now allowed to be with families and their loved ones until the end.

Dave L.

My first existential questions around death came when I was five years old and had started attending the parish Sunday school. The class for the younger children was run by two young teenage girls, who were supposed to watch us while we played and occasionally read us Bible stories. One Sunday, for some reason, it may have been a question from one of us kids, they decided to teach us about heaven and hell. The bottom line was that when we died, if we had been good, we went to heaven and if we had been bad, we went to hell. In heaven, we would dress up in our Sunday best and sing hymns all day and if we went to hell, we would be boiled in oil and stuck with pins. In their experience, all girls went to heaven, and all boys went to hell. Neither option was appealing to me and, if what my mother told me often was true, I was destined for hell, anyway. Wanting to investigate further, I asked my grandmother.

I had learned to be careful when asking my grandma questions because she had the habit of turning questions around so that I was the one who had to provide the answers. "Grandma, are you going to die?" When she had stopped laughing, she replied, "Of course, we all die, but don't worry, when you're my age, you'll understand all about death."

Fairly sure that I would get a straight answer, I asked, "Where will you go when you die?"

Again, I had to wait for her to stop laughing. "Well, first, they'll dig a big hole. Then they'll drop me in it and shovel all the earth on top of me." It struck me that it would have to be a very large hole as my grandma was a very large woman, but I already knew

Chapter 1

about graveyards and funerals, so I could live with her answers so far.

"Where do you go then?" As far as I was concerned, this was the gotcha question, but I hadn't counted on the infinite trickiness of grandmothers. "Then," she said, putting her arms around me, "The worms will come and eat me up," and she did her 'worms eating me up' impression.

When we'd both stopped laughing, I persisted, "And then where will you go?"

"Then," she said in a way that made me sure I'd get the answer I'd been looking for. "Then…the worms poop."

It was like a thousand flashbulbs going off at once. This was the first great insight into life's mysteries that I can remember. I knew all about worm poop because as it was my job when it rained (and it rained a lot where I grew up) to pick up all the worms that crawled up from between the flagstones in our yard and put them in my mother's garden, so the worm poop would fertilize the soil. To this small boy, the thought of turning into worm poop was heaven.

From then on, death became our favourite topic of conversation.

Cathy

I didn't think about death much at all until I got older. I'm not even sure I believed in it because I remember going to a funeral at a very young age, peering into the coffin and loudly exclaiming that she wasn't dead because I saw her move. You can imagine how that went over.

But then one friend's mother was killed in a car accident and another friend's mother died of cancer. I remember being struck by how final death is and how devastating it is for the people left behind.

Feelings About Death and Dying

Then, when I was in my 30's, I almost died. I had an ectopic pregnancy and by the time I realized it wasn't a really bad stomach-ache and went to the hospital, I had lost so much blood they didn't expect me to live. They took my then-husband into the chapel and told him to prepare for me not making it. I could hear them saying I had no blood pressure and was dying as I lay in the ER, but since it was completely out of my hands at that point, I was calm and unafraid. I suppose it could have been because my brain was deprived of oxygen, but whatever the reason, I remember looking at the crucifix above the door when they wheeled me into the operating room and thinking 'let thy will be done' even though I'm not religious. The doctor came in the next morning and said us skinny, wiry types have a way of pulling through. I was left with the feeling that death is nothing to be afraid of, that when the time comes and you're finished with the cycle of doing and becoming, you will feel acceptance and peace.

But then, two of my friends died — one by her own hand and the other from cancer, leaving a nine-year-old daughter behind. She fought to the end and did not go gentle into that good night. From that, I learned that death is not always preceded by acceptance and peace and that sometimes the will and the reasons to live are so strong that the person will resist and fight to the very end.

A few years ago, I took a stab in my journal about what I think happens after we die. The impetus came from my partner, Gary, coming back from visiting a dying friend at the hospital who had asked him 'if he thought there was an afterlife?' Gary being Gary — matter-of-fact and not one to sugarcoat things — said "no." He believed this is all there is. I think he saw me wince a bit because I thought he should have been more comforting. He asked me what I would have said. I would have replied something along the lines of our minds and experience can't begin to comprehend the universe we live in. We're part of that universe and that doesn't end when we die. I like to think that we merge back into the whole and it feels like coming home. Maybe some part of our earthly consciousness and awareness persevere that way. We are, after all, almost half made of stardust, particles formed in the big boom. Surely, they don't die when we do. I haven't a clue what form they take or how they continue to exist, nor do I really feel the need to have an answer. I understand the need to have something solid to believe in, but the truth is that no one knows.

Bobbie

As a child, funeral services usually had an open casket, and my parents didn't think it was appropriate for me to attend any funerals. Death was not talked about. My father was deployed overseas for five-and-a-half years and came home broken from what he had seen. Although he had nightmares until his passing, it was never talked about. It was a black cloud in our lives. The war changed everything for my parents and for me as well. My Dad often played the bagpipes at funerals, and I would go along with him and read my book or pass the time outside, waiting until he was finished. I didn't realize that I was really there to support him, so that he would come home afterwards, and there would be no drinking and less sadness. Death, for me, was sadness and tears.

My dad died when I was 18, and my world changed truly forever. I was so angry that life had treated my dad so harshly and I was so, so sad to have lost him. My mother and sister went back to Edmonton, and I was alone in BC. The ensuing years were hard for me. I was severely depressed and had no money. One afternoon, I had had enough. I took an overdose of pills and went to my dad's grave and went to sleep. I awoke in the hospital the next day with a doctor saying, "I don't know why someone so pretty would do this." I again knew that I was on my own and would have to find my own way.

Feelings About Death and Dying

I have been a hospice worker for 19 years and death, to me, is just another stage of life. I don't fear death for myself. I've made peace with the fact that it happens to everyone, but hurts the ones left behind the most.

Dave B.

The first instance of death's immediate presence came when I was 14, and my favourite aunt died. She'd been ill for some time, and no one really talked about it, until the evening my father came into my room and said, "You know your aunt is sick, don't you? Well, she's not going to get better." As a lifelong heavy smoker, she had lung cancer. For the last several months, she lay in her bed at home. She wanted to see me before she died, and I went into her bedroom. She was extremely gaunt and unable to speak much. She had something she wanted me to have and told me it was on the dresser and to take it. I didn't know what to do; I didn't know how to react. I just wanted to get out of that room, so I listened to her struggle to speak, and then I left without taking what she wanted me to have. I think I pretended not to understand her.

My mother did spend time with her, and my aunt told her the oft-heard story of being in a tunnel and seeing an opening ahead with daylight. She said she hadn't gone on to the end of the tunnel that time, but my mum was sure she did when she died.

I was a child of non-practicing Christians, and it was all 'when you die, you go to heaven if you're good.' I don't think I ever took the notion of heaven, the idea that you would be with your loved ones again, very seriously. For a while in my teens and into my twenties, I believed in reincarnation, which seemed comforting at the time.

I think I've only seriously grieved a death once in my life before Annie. It was after my friend died several years ago. With him, there was sadness that I'd almost written him off for most of the last 15 years. We only reconnected during his last few months, and the friendship remained there. I grieved the years we'd lost while not being in touch.

Annie's death is certainly the worst thing that has happened in my life. I am nowhere near 'over it' and doubt I ever will be.

Geneviève

I cannot recall talking about death much as I was growing up. It was not a concept a young family really focuses on. I knew that my mother's father died when she was only 13, but otherwise, my remaining grandparents were still alive, and our family seemed to have been blessed in avoiding tragic experiences.

I understood that people died. We had a neighbour who had lived through WWII and always told us stories, which included people dying. Grim, I know, for a child to hear. But otherwise, I blissfully went about living my life. I cannot recall friends having people in their lives dying, either.

It was not until I was about 17 that my grandfather died. I wasn't very upset by this because he was ill, and I did not know him very well. He was not a man who allowed you to get close to him. This may sound awful to say, but I was more upset about my family dog dying the following year. This was an animal I grew up with, and she had been with me most of my life.

I always thought that medical assistance in dying seemed like a very loving and humane way to die. I was a teenager when this concept was first introduced to me, hearing about how the Dutch were bringing in these new laws. It sparked great debate in our home. I recall how easy it was for me to say I believed in it. There was never a question in my mind.

Feelings About Death and Dying

Emily

As a child, my family never spoke about death or dying. My parents didn't really talk about it with me. The first death that I remember was my grandfather's, who died of cancer in the hospital when I was a teenager. I didn't grow up knowing my family and so it didn't affect me much, but I remember everyone was crying in the church and they all looked so sad, especially my mom, who was very close with him.

I watched my paternal grandmother take her last breath in the palliative care home when I was in my twenties. She was the first person I ever saw die. This was my first big loss. When I was growing up, she helped take care of me when my parents couldn't. I was so close to her. I didn't know how to grieve, and the thoughts and emotions that came up were new. Life wasn't the same without her; It was hard; I was sad most days and didn't want to be here. I wanted to be with her. My heart especially broke for my grandfather, who was now without his wife. I watched him distance himself from his family and no longer want to be around anyone during special occasions. Little did I know that someday this would be me.

Cynthia

I grew up in a Catholic home and attended Catholic school and church every Sunday. Everyone around me held the same beliefs, practiced the same rituals, and attended celebrations that looked pretty much identical. I started attending funerals at a pretty young age because we had the misfortune of losing four grandparents and two great grandparents, all within a few years of each another.

The funerals I attended all involved dark clothing, religious hymns, open caskets, prayers, and lots of crying. They were always followed by receptions in church halls with tables filled with crust-less sandwiches beside beverage stations tended by grey-haired church ladies.

One of my earliest memories is of kneeling in front of a casket as my mom leaned over and kissed her dead mother on the forehead. It struck me as odd that someone was there, wiping off the forehead of the corpse after each parishioner kissed her. I got in the Eucharist line again with my cousin and we knelt beside grandma daring one another to kiss her too. She felt cold.

Funerals became a lot like church on Sundays for me. I knew what to expect. I had most of the prayers and hymns memorized, and I found comfort in the rituals. People got old and then they died. You had a funeral and then buried them in the cemetery; they went to heaven and one day we all see each other again. In the summers, my mom would take us to the local florist to get fresh flowers and we'd go to the cemetery. We'd spend what felt like hours cleaning the family headstones, changing the flowers, and running around reading the epitaphs of the newest tragedies. I remember my favourites.

I was terrified, however, of my own parents dying. When we had babysitters, I used to pretend to sleep, and then lie awake waiting for my parents to come home, worrying about where I would have to go and live, if they didn't.

When I was 14, the rules broke. I went to a funeral for two sisters in their late teens who were killed together in a car accident. They weren't old. Everything I believed about death, everything I believed about the order of the world, and everything I had once had blind faith in, changed. The rituals and the order and the certainty stopped bringing me comfort, because I realized that they were just responses to tragedies, ways to attempt to bring order to chaos. But I saw and I felt the chaos, and wondered what kind of a God would allow these kinds of tragedies. So began my shift away from faith and towards embracing the chaotic, randomness of the world. I felt more comfort in accepting that there are no answers, than in searching for them and constantly being disappointed.

When my husband and I became parents, we decided to raise our kids without religion. We were living in the southern US around the time our kids began to ask questions about death and dying. We felt most comfortable telling them that what matters most in life is how you treat other people today, that when we die, our bodies become part of the earth, but what lives on is the memory of what we've accomplished and how we have made other people feel.

Brittney

Death was something I didn't like to think about too often growing up. It was never really brought up or discussed within my family. It was sort of 'taboo' I guess you could say. But it was something I dreaded, hated and worried about. I wasn't afraid of my death, but more so the death of others. I remember thinking that the very worst thing in the world for me would be losing both my mom and my dad. Just the thought would bring me to tears. What would I do without them? Losing them would have been the end of the world.

My great-grandmother died when I was about seven years old. I don't have a lot of memories about her passing, just attending the funeral, witnessing people crying and reminiscing around me, and my aunt bravely up front, reading off her well-written eulogy during the funeral. Since I was so young, I didn't really fully understand everything that goes along with dying, like grieving and heartache. I remember being silly with my cousin during the funeral and giggling about something which I now feel badly about.

I lost a friend in a car accident when I was 18. That was an intense, surreal and just flat out horrible time. My heart broke for his family, losing a child so young, and I experienced grief for the first

Chapter 1

time. It didn't seem real; I had just seen him a few weeks earlier. I was confused, sad, mad and had so many questions.

Now here I am, 33 years old, and both my parents are gone. I lost my mom and my dad in less than a year. My worst fear became a reality. I knew the day would come, but I never thought it would be this early on in my life. However, the world did not end. The world still turns, the sun still rises each morning and life goes on. "Why do bad things happen to good people?" I often wonder. I wish I knew the answer.

Now that I'm older and have experienced death, grieving, great sorrow and sadness firsthand, I don't feel scared of death, or feel worried about it. It's just a part of life. I truly believe there is life after death and I like to think that my loved ones who have departed are happy, healthy and are now angels up above, looking down on us.

Daimhin

When I was little and people would ask me my biggest fear, my answer was always the same: my loved ones dying. I had never put much thought into what happened after death, but it was still my biggest fear. When I thought about death, it always filled me with an intense feeling of dread. My stomach would turn to knots and if I thought about it long enough, I would get the urge to cry. The thought of having to live without my loved ones seemed unbearable and terrifying. When I would shake the feeling away, I would get a wave of relief knowing my family was intact and everyone was okay.

I am not a religious person and I do not believe in heaven or hell or an afterlife of any kind. I've imagined scenarios that include an afterlife, where loved ones watch over us, and we see them again. As comforting as it seems and as much as I'd like to believe it, my fact-seeking science brain cannot be convinced. I have always been drawn to facts, things that are tangible and things that can be explained. I believe that when you die, your heart stops beating, your brain stops, and you are left with a body with no one inside. Our bodies will return to the earth and the circle of life restarts.

Now that I have experienced death, loss and grief, I can say that I am probably more scared of death now than before. Before, I feared losing someone I loved and living without them. Now, I am very aware of how little time we all have on this earth and how every day is not promised, and that is almost scarier. That life is so finite is a very heavy thought to carry around daily.

What scares me now is that my future is not promised. The thought of dying young looms over many decisions I make daily, and a lot of them are driven by this fear. Where should I travel to next, how much to invest into retirement, should I go to the concert or event, or wait until the next time they come through? All these decisions are now heavily influenced by the fear that I may miss my opportunity.

Nikki

I did not have any positive emotions around death as I was growing up. It all seemed like doom and gloom. My parents shielded me from death, the dying, and even funerals. Death existed as something only adults had to deal with. I believed it would be something I wouldn't encounter until my older years. Death was something people dealt with relatively privately, and certainly not something to be discussed, celebrated or embraced as a normal part of life.

We were afraid of death and dying. I remember not wanting to visit my ailing grandparents in the hospital because I wanted to remember them as well and not sickly. I think this was actually me not wanting to face their decline because I was not prepared to deal with the emotions around death. Clearly, neither were the adults in my life.

Chapter 1

One of the first and only positive experiences I had with death stands in my memory, clear as day. I was probably about 10 years old. I attended my mother's best friend's father's funeral, and it was an open casket event. Seeing the dead body was quite unsettling, but then my father did something I found remarkable. He placed a few mini bottles of scotch in the pocket of "Uncle" Bruce's jacket and took his hand for a moment. It struck me as such a sweet offering and opened my eyes to the potential of having relationships with people beyond death. I know that very well now after losing my father. Our relationship continues to evolve, three and a half years later, and I have experienced a healing of our tumultuous relationship that I never imagined possible.

Robin

I've been relatively lucky in that I haven't lost many people. My nana died when I was 18 and my grandma died when I was 27. I never had grandfathers. I lost a friend in my twenties; he lived overseas and wasn't part of my daily life, but his death from cancer was heartbreaking and a reminder of how unfair life can be.

I don't have a particular faith, although I've grown up with the concept of heaven and the notion that people are reunited in the afterlife. I love this and want to believe it, but if I am completely honest, I don't. I think life just ends and that's that. To me, death has largely been something to dread, and something that's not talked about a lot.

I've faced questions about my own death through past struggles with depression and the thought that I really didn't want to suffer through another 40 years. Or maybe that's more a question of life. "Life is hard," people say. But that doesn't generally mean they want out of it.

Feelings About Death and Dying

I dreaded my parents' deaths for years, to the point where I talked to my therapist about it several years ago. "How do you prepare for that?!" I asked, knowing there was no good answer. I just didn't want to think about it.

I grieved my grandmothers' deaths, but they were elderly and had been sick. We knew it was inevitable. My dad had always been healthy, even as he got older. Then he got sick and declined fast and my question wasn't hypothetical anymore.

I'm realizing that when faced with someone's death, you're not only losing the person, but also who you are with them. I grieved my dad and the fact that he wouldn't see my kids grow up, but I also thought about who I would call when I had a car question and that if I saw a bird that I know he'd love, I wouldn't be able to tell him. I would no longer have 'my mom and dad's house' to go to.

Elizabeth

As a young girl, I often woke up scared whenever I had a nightmare about dying. There were always two very distinct, polar-opposite dreams which would repeat over and over. I would always wake up before I died, but as a child, it was terrifying. My nightmares focused on the actual moment of death and what led up to it. Death was always violent, but there was the unknown about what happened after a person died. It seemed to me that the unknown could almost be the worst part. Was that really the end, or was there something afterwards? My upbringing told me that there was nothing after death, but other people I knew were indicating that wasn't true.

Although my parents were not religious, I was expected to attend church as a child and go to Sunday school, but was allowed to decide for myself when I was a teenager, at which time I cut religion out of my life. Of course, I still didn't know what happens after a person dies, so l continued to fear the unknown.

Chapter 1

Years later, as a young adult, I was exposed to people who were very religious and wanted me to accept Christ as my personal saviour so that I could go to heaven. Of course, heaven was always portrayed as cloudlike, with pearly gates and so forth where you can live forever in bliss which isn't unappealing! By this time in my life, I was a fairly creative person and wanted to think that heaven could be true, but the analytical part of me was skeptical.

Other than my visions about death, my first encounter with death was when I was in high school. A very popular classmate was killed by a drunk driver on a Saturday night while coming home from a party. It felt shocking that this could happen to such a nice person. A while later, another student hung himself from the rafters in his family garage. His death brought up feelings of failure and guilt for me. I thought I should have seen some signs and been able to help him. I was shocked that young people around me would die. I had assumed only the elderly or very sick would face death. Since this was my first recollection of death, I suppose it validated my fears of dying being very violent.

Carol

When I was growing up, I never thought very much about death. I lost a great-grandmother and grandmother when I was young, but I never remember people being particularly sad. Both had lived long lives and their passing was seen as natural and not something to be all that upset about. My first experience of being truly sad about a death was when I was 18 and my aunt died. She had polio and had been in an iron lung for over 20 years. I remember feeling not so much sad for her, because she had been ill for a long time, but very sad for my dad who had adored his sister. I'd never seen my stoic dad upset before, and it jolted me.

The very sudden death of my mother-in-law when I was 34, and she was 71 hit me hard because I had to tell our four-year-old daughter where grandma had gone. I remember holding Julia on my lap and telling her that Grandma had gone away and couldn't come back. I didn't have good words to explain death. My daughter wanted to know where Grandma was, and I said something about her floating away from the earth. Suddenly, my daughter started to sob and sob. She said she remembered being 'out there' and that it was dark and how alone and afraid she'd felt. I didn't know what to make of what she said, and I still don't.

I was with my father when he died in 2012, but my mom and I saw his passing from complications related to Alzheimer's as a blessing. He was deteriorating rapidly, and we were about to make the gut-wrenching decision to put him in long-term care. My gratitude that he was able to die peacefully at home with us at his side still influences how I feel about his death. I just can't feel sad because I know he didn't want to live with Alzheimer's anymore. Six years later, in 2018, my brother also died from complications related to early onset Alzheimer's at the age of 65. Although I mourn him, I saw his death as a blessing. He had already gone into long-term care, and it was pretty grim.

I'm not particularly afraid of death for myself, but I do worry about losing more of the people I love. My heart is too fractured to survive another blow any time soon.

Andrée

I was 8 years old when I had my first experience with death. My maternal grandmother, whom I was very close to and loved very much, died of heart disease. When my parents received the news, they immediately flew to Quebec City, but we were not told why they were going away. It wasn't until they returned a week later that we learned of grandma's passing. Being raised Catholic, I was told she was in heaven, which was comforting to me as a young child.

Chapter 1

When I was a young adult, both of my paternal grandparents died. Although I was sad, I felt they had lived good lives, raised nine children and it was natural for them to die.

I did not reflect on death and dying or focus on what happens after you die until my mother died. She was only 58, and I was 37, when she died of lung cancer, which was far too young to die, in my opinion. It did not make sense to me that we just stop existing when we die. I liked the idea that we might see one another again. I continue to believe that there must be something greater than us in the universe.

Twenty years later, when my 31-year-old daughter was dying, I felt comforted knowing that she would be reunited with her father. She wouldn't be alone on the other side. I also find comfort in being able to talk to them whenever I need to.

Some might say it is a coping mechanism, having lost so many of my loved ones, but I believe that those who die are still with us.

Shannon

Growing up, my family never discussed death, faith or religion at all. I remember death being very somber and sad, just by the way my parents behaved after one of their friends had passed or my grandfather. It was all very 'hush, hush' and danced around. It was mysterious. I was intrigued even as a child. Where did they go? Will we see each other again? Why do we have funerals?

I remember seeing my first dead body. I was a respiratory therapy student, and my preceptor asked me to go retrieve some equipment, not knowing an elderly woman's body was still in the room. I waltzed through the curtain and there she laid, silent, pale and still.

I was surprised by the peace and calm I initially felt behind the curtain. The noise of a chaotic Intensive Care Unit seemed to fade away. She had chosen not to escalate her care to include breathing tubes or chest compressions. The room was tidy; cards from family and friends covered the bedside table. I remember staring down at her, wondering what her life had held and who was feeling her loss.

It wasn't until I considered her loved ones that I suddenly became very aware of my own beating heart, skipping at a faster pace than usual. I considered my loved ones' mortality, the reality of the career I had chosen, the fragility of what it means to be alive. I felt vulnerable. Exposed. Powerless. Human.

That was 12 years ago, and since then as a respiratory therapist, I've been the hands that help initiate life support; and discontinue it at times to allow for death to take place. I've experienced many deaths as an outsider, a provider, someone on the periphery. Death was fascinating to me. It often felt like a monumental fight to prevent death from occurring. As I witnessed the enormity of human suffering that the medical system can induce and prolong, my heart would ache for anyone suffocating under a shred of hope that their loved one could possibly recover while scientific evidence had stacked the odds against them.

When Medical Assistance in Dying was legalized in 2016, I had a sense of relief, not only for patients and families, but for all the bedside healthcare providers as well. It can often feel as if we are torturing patients, allowing for greater suffering than any human should be forced to endure, let alone choose, especially with little chance of a meaningful recovery. Death is often not the most difficult circumstance I encounter at work. I also know that death does not always have to include suffering, at least not prolonged suffering.

Chapter 1

Carole

At various stages of my life, I've pondered the supreme question, 'What happens after death?' and held diverse beliefs. As a youngster, I was certain that I'd meet up with grandparents, my dog, etc., in an idyllic setting. Somehow, it was always a lush, flower filled, sunny meadow. I had pictured the warm, loving embrace of my grandmother and an exuberant greeting from my beloved dog, Whiskey. These thoughts were comforting and somewhat alleviated the immense feelings of sadness and loss that accompanied the abandonment.

As a younger adult, I read several popular self-help type books and as a result started to entertain the notion of reincarnation — sometimes returning as an animal (bird was my naïve selection), and other times as a progressively improved human being. It was frightening to imagine that death was 'the end,' so the idea of returning as a soaring eagle invoked feelings of immense awe and freedom. Flying high over tall trees, enjoying the vastness and beauty of our planet — the appeal of this was so wonderfully exhilarating!

Now, as an older adult, my speculation has evolved into two rather diverse 'trains of thought.' The first is the rather basic: nothing, the end, finito. The second is more complex to understand and explain. As a physicist with an interest in String Theory, I'm willing to accept the possibility of other dimensions that are currently unknown to us. Could we exist in some form in another dimension after our death?

One fundamental deduction I realized several years ago was that I don't actually dread death itself. It's the process of dying that causes me angst. The natural aging process and the usual accompanying ailments have instilled this fear of discomfort, pain and loneliness.

Feelings About Death and Dying

If I lose mobility, my wonderful, active, social world will shrink. Other medical issues could involve so many procedures that dependency on others would be necessary, which fills me with both anxiety and alarm.

If death truly is 'the end,' I accept that, but I have this strong desire to leave something of 'me' that will somehow be preserved for future generations.

CHAPTER 2 -

DIAGNOSIS: BEGINNING OF THE

END

Hope means hoping when everything seems hopeless.
- Gilbert K. Chesterton

For many of us who tell our stories in *The Many Faces of MAID*, the journey towards the end – the Medically Assisted Death (MAID) of our loved one – began with an ailment or a diagnosis. Our person had cancer or another terminal illness or faced irreversible decline because of age, injury or 'clinical frailty.' Alternatively, our person was searching for a diagnosis and clinging to hope, while at the same time dealing with the suspicion that they may never improve.

What were these experiences like? Which emotions erupted and which lurked beneath the surface or stayed pushed way down and avoided? How did we – the MAID storytellers – feel and react in certain moments during the early days of our journeys?

Over the weeks, months and sometimes years leading to the death of our loved one, all of us experienced a huge range of emotions – expected and unexpected, difficult and easy, and some that were challenging to identify or even name. Almost all of us felt all the emotions, but nobody felt them in the same order or on the same day or even at the same moment. For some, one emotion dominated for hours or days, while for others, the emotions shifted and changed in a chaotic storm.

While you likely know that it's 'normal' to experience many different emotions, and that each person's reaction to a situation is unique, you may take comfort knowing that you are not the only one who has felt a certain way at various stages of your journey — and that it's absolutely fine not to feel like you thought you would — or should.

In this chapter, our storytellers share some emotions we felt at the beginning of our journey towards a loved one's death with MAID.

DENIAL

When faced with terrible news, or even the creeping realization that someone's health may not improve, denial is a logical retreat. What better way to cope than to deny that anything bad is happening?

Of course, denial only takes us so far, but for both Cynthia and Carol, denial played a major role in how they navigated the beginning of the end.

Carol

My mother never had a diagnosis, just a long, slow decline over a period of about six months during which she started suffering from crippling anxiety. Every day I tried to convince myself I could find a way to 'fix' her, that of course her decline was temporary. I did everything I could to help her, but nothing worked — doctors, books, therapies, drugs, long supportive chats, home care — you name it, I tried it. She got increasingly more anxious, her physical health eventually weakening to a point where she could no longer cope with the independent living facility she was living in and had to be moved to a facility with two higher levels of care—assisted living and long-term care.

For all the months of her decline, I was positive that Mom's end was nowhere in sight. Sure, she was almost 94, and of course I knew she couldn't live forever, but I counted on at least a few more years of having her play an active role in my life and the catalyst around which our small family revolved. Living without my daily chats with Mom was unthinkable! She was my rock. For at least twenty years, she'd call every night at 10 pm and we'd chat about the state of the world, the family, my work, and her many activities. I could always depend upon Mom to listen and to provide wise advice.

And then her daily calls started coming two or three times a day, and were no longer pleasant chats, but cries for help. She even started saying, "I wish I could jump off a bridge." In my ferocious desire to pretend that everything was 'just fine,' I refused to take these statements seriously. Everything would be just fine if I could only find the right book, the right doctor, the right pill to get Mom better. Of course, Mom didn't want to die. That was the anxiety talking; she'd be back to her old self in no time. I needed to work harder to find a solution.

On the day Mom moved to the new assisted living facility, she was so unwell we had to move her instead to a long-term care bed (and were extremely lucky one was available). For two months, we rented both the care room and the more spacious assisted living room. All her stuff was moved in and divided between the two rooms. Despite watching her grow weaker and weaker and more and more anxious, I was convinced she'd soon be moving into assisted living to resume her regular, independent life with just a little more help.

I refused to even entertain the notion that her journey away from me was beginning. She would get back to her practical, cheerful, smart self. The debilitating attacks during which she'd cry and tell me she wanted to die would soon be a bad memory. She had to get better. We had a cruise planned!

Cynthia

I will never forget sitting alone in the empty imaging department and hearing the staff from inside the control room, with the door ajar, laughing, joking, normal co-worker type banter, while my future hung in the balance. I remember thinking, what will be a better outcome, finding out he's had a stroke, or finding out he hasn't? Then I heard "Can someone call the doctor? This guy has a tumour."

I knew that the only other patient having a CT scan was a woman, but I still somehow convinced myself that the technicians couldn't be talking about my husband. He was in there because of a suspected stroke, not a brain tumour. I continued texting my cranky neighbour about our ongoing garbage can squabble, trying not to focus on what I'd just heard because surely, I had heard wrong. I noticed that this waiting room felt eerily empty. It was so damn QUIET. Millions of thoughts raced through my mind as I accompanied my husband on the relatively short walk back to the chaotic ER waiting room.

They weren't talking about him.

Or were they?

How unprofessional, to talk so crassly about a patient like that.

It's him, it has to be. They said HE. That other patient was female.

No, no, no. It's not him. It's not him.

But what if it is?

No, it can't be.

My stomach hurts. I think I might throw up.

Have I eaten today? I'm starving.

The voice in my head went round in circles, like a record stuck on repeat. My phone vibrated in my pocket; our friends had arrived with food and were waiting at the entrance to the emergency room.

Our butts had barely landed back in the hard plastic hospital seats when the ER doctor appeared, summoning us to a quiet place where we could talk.

HOLY SHIT! In the ER, good news doesn't come this fast. My heart sank, my stomach lurched, my knuckles whitened as my grip on my purse tightened. I knew. I knew exactly what he was about to tell us. I'd already heard it, hadn't I?

Please don't say it! I pleaded silently. If he didn't say it, it couldn't be true. His lips moved, his eyes softened, and his shoulders sagged as he officially delivered the words I had already heard but willed the universe to make false.

My world, my future, our hopes and dreams, crumbled, crashing in on top of themselves. Tears. Shock. Denial.

Food. I need to go pick up the food.

How Do You Feel?
Did denial play a role in how you reacted to a terminal diagnosis or to finding out that your person wasn't going to get better? Take some time to write about or reflect on how denial affected you.

Diagnosis: The Beginning of the End

SHOCKED

When a diagnosis comes out of the blue, as it did for several of our storytellers, it is understandable that the first emotions may be shock or disbelief. How can this be happening? Why? I don't believe it! I *can't* believe it! In an instant, our lives are turned upside down and we are powerless to do anything about it.

Daimhin shares what shock felt like for her when her father's terminal diagnosis was confirmed.

Daimhin

My mom took the day off work to go with my dad to his appointment. Already, I knew that the likelihood of good news was slim; the doctors were just confirming what we already knew — that the tumour was malignant. As soon as I saw my dad's face as he walked in the door, I knew he didn't have good news. My heart was racing as my parents told my sister and me to sit down. Although they were expected, the words leaving my dad's mouth hit me one by one, like individual daggers lodging themselves into my heart.

My dad had cancer. *How is this happening to me? This is what happens in books and movies and to other people. Not to me. Not to my family. How unfair.* It was my worst nightmare. My family moved around me in slow motion. My brain felt like it was frozen as if it had been sitting in ice water, every thought moving slowly through the fog. I cried, but the reality of the situation had not quite made its way through the empty white space that was occupying my head. *This isn't real. It can't be. Wake up. Just wake up.*

My slow thoughts were interrupted by my dad. He broke the ice in his usual humorous fashion; "Don't worry, the Tom Baker Cancer Center has 5 stars on Yelp."

45

Chapter 2

How Do You Feel?
How did shock affect you when coping with the diagnosis of your loved one?

CONFUSED

One moment, life is predictable and orderly, and the next, our loved one receives a terminal diagnosis, and both our lives are thrown into chaos. We feel confused and disoriented. The once solid earth begins to liquify beneath our feet.

For Shannon, one of the strongest emotions she experienced was confusion after finding out about her close friend's cancer.

Shannon

After the initial shock wore off, I found myself wildly confused. It was like I had been violently slapped square in the face by the reality of Wendy's diagnosis and her rapidly dwindling time here on this earth. My ears rang. My face got hot. My jaw clenched as I tried to stuff down whatever emotions were trying to emerge.

I was so unprepared for what Wendy was telling me. My stomach churned as I recalled the anguish that only followed death. I shuddered when I realized I would soon feel this anguish again. But Wendy was sitting right in front of me. She was laughing. We were talking about hockey now. The conversation went from Stage IV cancer to Jenner and Poulin and the Canadian Women's National Hockey Team.

I left the coffeehouse that sunny day with nothing but questions, confusion, and a deep hot anger that, for the moment, I stuffed away.

How Do You Feel?

Write about any feelings of confusion you may have experienced as a result of hearing your loved one's diagnosis.

FEARFUL

Fear was perhaps one of the most common emotions felt by our storytellers as they embarked upon the journey towards death with their loved one. They experienced a fear of death, of course, but also fear of the unknown and fear that they may not be able to cope.

Dave B. and Brittney share how fear affected them following the diagnosis of their loved one.

Dave B.

After Annie's CT scan, the technologist led her by the arm to Emergency and told her to see a doctor there. Panic arrived in our world. Panic for me anyway; I wondered if Annie somehow knew already. A couple of days later, she had emergency surgery. After she was recovering on the ward, the surgeon dropped in and told us, "It's definitely not cancer." Panic receded for me, while a lower-level fear for Annie crept in. *If it's not cancer, what is it? And why is her speech being affected?*

She came home to her own bed, but she was very ill from the surgery. Vomiting was pretty constant for a few weeks; her mysterious motor-neuron symptoms made it hard to eat, but she couldn't keep much down, anyway. I felt fearful and helpless as I took care of her, bathing her, taking her to the toilet, and helping her get dressed.

We waited four weeks for the final diagnosis. We met the surgeon at her office and got a rundown of diet issues and then the

Chapter 2

offhand question, "Now, are you ready for the really bad news?" The diagnosis was Stage 4 colon cancer, with a prognosis of four to five years, assuming she had chemo. We were dumbstruck because we had been so sure that Annie didn't have cancer, but something else that could be cured.

I felt quite self-absorbed upon hearing the diagnosis, and then on the way out of the office and on the drive home. I have no sense of how Annie felt on receiving that 'existential slap.' My only memory of the immediate aftermath was arriving home and standing at the bottom of the stairs. She went to the next step and then turned around and we kissed long and hard. I think we were too numb to speak, and anyway, by this time, she was having a hard time getting words out. We were both weeping and could do nothing but hold each other tightly.

Fear of what her illnesses were taking away from her was strong in me. And there was another fear that I'm not proud of, and it boiled down to, *what about me? Was this the end of 'us?'*

Was I going to be alone again?

Would I be able to manage?

Could I survive on my own?

Who would I sit with in bed in the mornings and talk with? Who was going to cut my hair? What if I got COVID? Who would look after me?

My fears were justified. Nobody is going to look after me.

Brittney

The day I found out my mom was sick feels like just yesterday. I was living an hour away from home, but I would go home every other weekend. I loved it. I'd drive home after work, just in time to have dinner with my mom and stepdad, Tom. Then, my mom would help me with my laundry, and I would end the day by having a bath in the wonderful soaker tub that overlooks

Diagnosis: The Beginning of the End

Georgian Bay. My mom and I would take the dogs for a walk together, go into town to get groceries, and go for lunch. It was my home away from home. It felt cozy and safe, being surrounded by family, sleeping in, having a nice home-cooked meal, and bringing clean laundry and leftovers back with me. It was the best 'warm and fuzzy' feeling. And honestly, it was so hard to leave when I had to go back to 'reality.'

It was the end of April. The harsh Ontario winter had finally come to an end, and it was one of the first 'nice' days of the spring. I sat out on the back deck on the chaise lounge to bask in the warm sun. I knew my mom had an appointment that day with the ear/nose/throat specialist that her dentist had referred her to, although she hadn't told us much about the jaw pain she was experiencing. I could feel the fear in the air that morning as I realized that my mom was nervous. We all knew she had a pain in her mouth/jaw area because she'd been to the dentist a few weeks prior and been referred to the specialist. I felt uneasy and anxious; my hands were sweaty all day. Something felt 'off,' almost as if my mom already knew what this specialist was going to tell her.

As I sat out on the deck reading, I remember thinking that my mom and Tom had been gone for a while. Finally, I heard the door open and close and the dogs jumping up and down, happy to see Mom and Tom finally at home. My mom came out to the deck, sat down next to me, looked at me with her sad, worried eyes and said, "It's cancer." My heart sank. My world turned upside down. I wanted to puke. I wanted to scream.

What the hell, is this real life? She started crying, and I hugged her. I started crying too.

It was just a pain in her mouth and it's cancer? What? I was so scared. There were talks of surgery, radiation, chemo, more CT and MRI scans, etc.

Chapter 2

I had to drive home that evening and I remember Tom said to me, "It's worse than what she is letting on" as he helped me put my bags in the car. I cried the whole way home as the fear grew inside of me. *Would she lose part of her jaw? Would she be able to eat normal food?* I had to pull over at least once to get a hold of myself. I was scared as hell. I felt so nauseous. My stomach was in knots, and I felt like I never wanted to eat again. My life had just changed, HER life had just changed, my family's life had just changed, all in a blink of an eye. How would I be able to go into work the next day and act like my normal, bubbly self when all I wanted to do was get more answers and for my mom to be okay? It was the worst feeling imaginable.

One of my biggest fears was losing a parent. Starting that day, that fear sat on my shoulders like a fifty-pound weight for the next five years.

How Do You Feel?
Take some time to write about the role fear played in your journey. How did it manifest in your body?

APPREHENSIVE

Apprehension is defined as a foreboding that something bad or unexpected is about to happen.

Jane shares the apprehension she felt after hearing her husband's diagnosis.

Jane

Apprehension was the first emotion that gripped me as we sat in the doctor's office waiting to hear the results of my husband's numerous tests. His breathing had become more laboured, and we

Diagnosis: The Beginning of the End

thought his asthma had been acting up. First came the x-rays. Waiting outside the x-ray room came thoughts of *what if it's not asthma? What if it really is something this time?* My stomach lurched as I thought about lung cancer. I quickly dismissed the thought as we had been down this road before. I lived with a man who imagined that every pain or ill feeling was a major disease that would be fatal.

Then the call came from the doctor's office that he wanted a pulmonary function test and an office appointment. Once again sitting outside listening to my husband having the test, I became tense and felt like my body was going to seize up. I think somewhere deep down I knew that this time the outcome was not going to be positive.

We sat in the office nervously looking at the computer screen. It was hard to figure out what we were looking at. The doctor started to explain: "You have idiopathic pulmonary fibrosis." My world tilted — there was something wrong, but the news wasn't what we expected. And then relief. It wasn't lung cancer.

But what was it? The doctor explained that my husband would slowly lose the ability to breathe because his lungs would become hard.

Then the questions started. *What was the cure?* None! *How long?* Five years maybe? *What about treatment ... medications, oxygen, homecare?* I tried to put on my chaplain hat and sit calmly listening to the answers to our questions, but panic started to rise.

Here was a man who, despite his imaginings of dread, was strong and proud and who always cared for others. I was overwhelmed with apprehension and dread. I just kept staring at the computer screen while my head swam with thoughts and questions of how my husband would cope with not being able to do the things he wanted. *What would our lives be like? How would the end come? How would we both cope?*

Chapter 2

How Do You Feel?

Write about any feelings of apprehension you may have experienced as a result of hearing your loved one's diagnosis.

HELPLESS

A feeling of helplessness often occurs after receiving terrible news. Few things are more challenging in life than knowing that you can do nothing to make things better, no matter how much you want to or how hard you try.

Elizabeth shares how helpless she felt when she learned about her mother's diagnosis.

Elizabeth

My mother was so wonderful at staying in touch on a regular basis. Usually, once a week, she would reach out to me and my siblings. We all lived in different parts of the world, so it was very important to her to be in contact with everyone.

I was having a normal busy day, tending to our family, trying to make a meal, run a business and do all the things that consume the day of a working woman. Mom called for one of our usual chats and once we dispensed with the basics, she told me that she had been diagnosed with CLL (a form of leukemia that is not curable). The bottom dropped out of my world. I was crying, but also trying to stay strong. I was in shock and felt sick, knowing that my world would never be the same again. I immediately wanted to rush to be with my mom and hug her, but that wasn't possible.

We got off the phone, and I had a full ugly crying session while I broke the news to my husband.

Diagnosis: The Beginning of the End

With CLL, there is a certain 'wait and see' period, where the medical team monitors blood counts, among other things. For a long period of time, nothing was being done. Back then, I couldn't understand why no medical intervention was happening. My mind was racing. *What about chemotherapy? What about a bone marrow transplant? What about radiation?* I was confused and angry that I couldn't do anything for her and frustrated that the doctors seemed to be just letting the cancer grow within her body. At that point, the feeling of complete hopelessness settled in. I was prepared to drop everything that was going on in my life to go and donate bone marrow, but as a result of Mom's age, that wasn't an option. I was going to lose my mother and I couldn't do a single thing about it.

About six years into my mom's journey with CLL, my father was diagnosed with colon cancer. He started radiation and surgery was scheduled. At this point, I was facing the prospect of losing both of my parents at perhaps the same time. I felt nauseated and sick, stressed and hopeless all at once.

Dad's diagnosis and treatment happened so fast, whereas with Mom, it seemed to be moving as slowly as molasses running uphill.

Unfortunately, my father developed peripheral neuropathy as a side effect of the chemotherapy drugs he was given. No amount of medication or the multitudes of other things that were suggested to him gave him any relief. The suffering was terrible to witness and made me feel even more helpless. I just wanted to be able to do something for him.

Why couldn't the doctors help him? We sometimes forget that the doctors are not in fact gods, and that they don't have all the answers. Even though my father had told his oncologist that he was starting to develop nerve problems, she told him it wasn't permanent and to keep going with the drugs that had been prescribed. If he had listened to his body a bit more, and questioned the doctors a bit more, things might have been different for him. I was so incredibly incensed that this could happen, and I felt a seething anger towards this doctor whom I had never met but wanted to hold to account in some way.

As my father's pain increased, my mom's health was quickly declining.

With two parents having cancer at the same time and me living 3000 miles away, I felt completely helpless.

How Do You Feel?
Did you feel helpless? How did you feel knowing that you wouldn't be able to make things better for your loved one?

DISCOURAGED

A terminal diagnosis is often accompanied by months and years of treatments. Some treatments work for a while, and some have little chance of success, but at least trying them is doing *something*. We are used to putting our faith in medicine, but what do we do when medical interventions fail?

Andrée shares how discouraged she felt upon learning that the treatments available to her daughter, Kim, would give her another five years at most.

Andrée

When my daughter's cancer stopped responding to treatments, they told us, "If she doesn't get a stem cell transplant, she could die."

We needed to find her a donor. I made a mental list of the people who might be able to donate. We were told there was a 25%

chance her sister could be a match, which seemed so small. I was scared to get my hopes up. *What if she wasn't a match?* It could take months to find a donor.

The doctors suggested Kim move to Montreal for a month so she could receive full body radiation that was not available in Ottawa. They said that maybe it would help put her cancer into remission. If Kim moved to Montreal, I would have to go with her to help care for her. I felt so discouraged and tired. It seemed like it was just one hurdle after another. All I could think about was how desperately I didn't want her to die.

I did a bit of research on stem cell transplants. I read that a transplant is considered 'successful' if the person survives for one year, two years, five years. *How can that be the definition of success? How is living for five more years a success when you are only 25 years old?* I want Kim to grow old with her new husband, buy her first house, have children and a career, live her dreams. That would be success — being in remission would be a success. Living a few more years didn't feel acceptable. My heart ached for her, for her young husband, and for me. I didn't want to bury my daughter. I held back my tears when we were together and tried to stay positive and keep going, but most days, I just wanted to scream.

So much for this being 'an old man's disease.' *She has her whole life ahead of her. This is so unfair!*

How Do You Feel?
Did you feel discouraged by the medical interventions available to your loved one following their diagnosis? How did you cope knowing that treatment may not be successful?

Chapter 2

ANGRY

Although anger can be a destructive emotion, it's an understandable reaction to life-altering news. Most storytellers felt anger at some point in our journeys. Why me? It's not fair! I don't deserve this! Allowing yourself to feel anger can provide you with a much-needed way to vent frustration.

Nikki shares how anger affected her while dealing with her father's illness.

Nikki

The irony stings. The feeling in my chest is hot and searing. We are back at the doctor's office for another useless appointment. The butterfly mobile on the ceiling that is meant to please me just annoys me. Nobody is helping me. It feels like I'm drowning. I'm sinking and shifting in my chair because I can't even stand being in my own skin. I'm pissed. He has been telling me, crying to me, that he wants to die for three years. Three fucking years of me doing everything in my power to take as good care of him as possible, even when he's been such an asshole to me.

I'm angry and resentful. The guy who raised me and called me useless, always comparing me to my brother and asking why I wasn't more like him. *Well, where is my brother now? Why am I the one sitting here, in the doctor's office (AGAIN!), for what feels like another day-long appointment that leaves me completely drained of any energy?* My blood is boiling, and my ears are burning.

Oh, the irony. The 'useless' daughter is now managing and taking Dad to all of his appointments with doctors, specialists, surgeons. The 'useless' daughter has come to his rescue every time he has needed to go to the hospital. The 'useless' daughter who has literally wiped his ass and picked him up off the floor, only to put him back together while he continues to verbally assault me and drink. The 'useless' daughter who goes to the grocery store and picks up the six slices of honey ham he wants, even though I work full time and have two young kids.

Where is everyone else? I'm so mad at my mom and brother in this moment that I could just scream at the top of my lungs. But I feel like I've been screaming and drowning in the responsibility of taking care of my dad for years and when I scream, no sound comes out. Nobody hears me or sees me. I'm tired. My body doesn't even feel like mine anymore. It's like a dead weight that I just drag around like an old heavy suitcase. The sense of duty and owing is crushing me.

Where is my brother, my dad's Golden Child that I never measured up to? My mother's words telling me how proud she is for what I am taking on, land like specks of dust. They mean nothing to me. They actually just fuel the uncontrollable fire of anger that now permanently lives inside of me. I can't see beyond how much I resent them all. I tell myself "Ok, Nikki. Put your smile on and thank the doctor for his time."

How Do You Feel?
Did you feel angry at the beginning of your person's journey? How did that anger manifest for you? Were you angry at the doctors? At yourself? At your loved one? At others?

BETRAYED

Coping with adverse events can lead us to feel as if we've been betrayed. Didn't we have a bargain with the universe to stay alive? How can that bargain be reneged upon?

For one storyteller, the hopelessness that consumed her following her husband's terminal diagnosis led to deep feelings of betrayal.

Chapter 2

Anonymous

What did I feel when the final blow fell? Betrayed, that's how I felt. The words 'no more hope' were never uttered by our oncologist, but the words that were uttered by him, 'pathologist's report,' 'clonal plasma cells…more than 20%' echoed without comprehension in my mind. The doctor asked, "any questions?" before departing for his long weekend. We weren't sure what we had just heard. We knew it wasn't good. Our confusion sucked us into a whirlpool of not knowing if we were about to be sucked down or spit out.

When we confirmed the diagnosis with an on-call oncologist the next day, we knew, without doubt, that there was 'no more hope.' The progress of the cancer would outstrip the treatment's ability to keep up. A thundercloud entered the room, robbing it of all light and all colour, sucking the oxygen out of the air and leaving us gasping for air like fish stranded on a dry riverbed.

With the realization that there was no more hope, I turned to my husband — the most positive, optimistic, full-of-life-being I had ever known — and witnessed the light in his eyes go out. There would be no more planning life around treatment appointments. Hope had been sucked out of our beings. My head exploded. My eyes stopped seeing. This was it. The end. He didn't get five to twelve years after diagnosis like they'd promised. He was only getting eleven months. We had done everything we had been advised to do. We'd followed the regimes and the schedules, had lived with the side effects and had kept going back for more.

For nothing.

I felt absolute and utter betrayal. Would we have been better off saying 'f' it and gone on living our lives to the fullest? Ah, but we couldn't because, well, COVID. Betrayed pretty much sums it up for me. Hope was a nasty little joke.

How Do You Feel?

Write about any feelings of betrayal you may have experienced after hearing your loved one's diagnosis.

SADNESS

For most of our storytellers, facing the reality that our loved one was dying led to profound feelings of sadness. While not an unexpected reaction, the feeling of sadness can be overwhelming, disorienting, and all-consuming.

Sadness was a dominant emotion for both Robin and Bobbie.

Robin

When my dad got a lung disease, I, too, felt short of breath.

There was no one moment of diagnosis, just a steady increase in symptoms that, through the power of denial, I was able to explain away. Denial is a powerful emotion, but when it goes away, it leaves a wide-open door for other feelings to enter, and for me, that was a deep, aching sadness. It felt like a heaviness in my chest that settled in and wouldn't leave.

When my dad coughed, I found myself holding my breath. I wondered how long the coughing would last, and as I waited, I felt myself pause on a shallow inhale. My breath no longer flowed freely; it just sat in my chest.

In the space of a year, my dad went from being an active man who still worked and gardened to one who spent his time sitting in a chair hooked up to oxygen. I had no idea what to do to help him, so I just put on a brave face and pretended everything was okay. It clearly wasn't. I watched him walk around the house, maneuvering carefully around corners and the banister at the top of the stairs so he didn't snag his oxygen tube. I picked up the tube to help him and made sure my kids didn't race down the stairs and yank it.

I just wanted to wind back the clock and get back the dad I knew.

I slowly started acknowledging the what-if question and asked my therapist how I could possibly prepare myself for my dad's death. I wanted it to be a mature, thoughtful question, but as soon as I asked it, my face crumpled, and the tears came. I went from barely breathing to taking deep, gulping breaths while I cried.

When I think about my dad now, that ache in my chest is still there, and I have to remind myself to take a deep breath as I let the tears fall. It feels exactly like the broken heart emoji—a giant crack, splitting right down the centre. And I still need to remind myself to breathe.

Bobbie

It was such a beautiful, warm spring day. Bob was feeling a bit guilty taking a day off school to go see the doctor, something he rarely did since he was always a super healthy guy. I wasn't too worried; we had seen the neurologist a year before and came away with no diagnosis. But because Bob was so fit and aware of his body, he had become concerned when he noticed his thumb twitching. He could feel other things, but this was the only visible change.

As soon as we walked into the neurologist's office, he immediately stood up and came over to Bob. He said, "I am so sorry, but you have Parkinson's" and then led Bob to a chair. I was frozen. The doctor turned and asked me to sit. I was thinking that, of course, he must be wrong; Bob hadn't even had any tests, and besides, we'd just walked in!

The rest of the appointment was a blur for me. I didn't cry. Instead, I was thinking ahead and was terrified, and also so worried about my husband, whose fitness was so important to him. I wished immediately that it was me. I couldn't get that out of my mind. We left the office holding hands tightly. We just sat in the car, in a dark and dreary underground parking lot, holding hands and not talking.

Finally, Bob said, "Let's not waste the sunshine" and we drove to the market and walked along the water, not talking, only stopping occasionally to share huge hugs as we tried to process our future. I felt terrified, shocked, and so very, very sad for my husband. I didn't cry—and I always cry—because I could feel that he needed me. If I cried, he would falter, and he was trying so hard to be strong. When we got back to the car, we hugged and Bob said, "I am going to be fine and together we will be okay."

 We had to put our dog Keta to sleep two weeks later, and we finally wept the buckets of tears we had been holding in. Saying goodbye to our adored dog gave us permission to cry and be sad—not only for her, but for the life that we had shared up to that point. It was a last treasured gift from Keta.

How Do You Feel?
How did sadness manifest itself for you? How did it affect your body? Did you resist feeling the sadness? Perhaps push it to the back of your mind? Did it overwhelm you?

HOPELESS

For many storytellers, feelings of hopelessness crept in while we tried to cope with a terminal diagnosis or the knowledge that our loved one wasn't going to get better. How can we possibly carry on without hope?

Chapter 2

Geneviève shares the hopelessness she experienced following her husband's Alzheimer's diagnosis.

Geneviève

The diagnosis for my husband's illness came a little over a year after he suspected something was wrong.

It all began with my listening to the flashing light alert on the answering machine, reminding my husband of his upcoming appointment with our GP. This surprised me because my husband always needed a major push to go see a doctor about anything.

When I questioned him, he said it was a routine appointment, and that there was nothing to worry about and left to go exercise, but when he came back, he sat me down and talked to me about his concerns. I was stunned! *What do you mean, your brain is not functioning well? What do you mean you're having a hard time remembering things? What do you mean you sometimes can't remember what to do next?* He was 54. I hit a solid concrete wall and did not know what to do, where to turn, or what to expect.

Needless to say, I went with him to his doctor's appointment and all subsequent ones.

Tests revealed that we needed to see a neurologist, who after more tests and a very long year of uncertainty about his future, my future, our future, revealed that he had Young Onset Alzheimer's Disease.

To see it written down almost makes it seem like it was nothing, but it was not nothing. My world turned upside down. *How could this be?* I wanted to throw up. My husband was one of the kindest, most loved people I knew. This could not be happening! There is a certain kind of hopelessness that invades when the person you love has been given such a diagnosis. *There is no cure. What now? How long before he gets really bad? How long do we have together? How long has this been going on? Was most of our lives together a sort of lie, since maybe he was not always himself?* Here I had thought at times that he didn't love me anymore because he didn't always remember what we had just talked about. I thought he had lost interest in me, but no, it was this damn disease.

In all honesty, hope is everything. It is part of our wellbeing. If you don't have it, what is the point? So how can you properly deal with any situation when you know there is no hope? To realize that you can't do anything, even when you're willing to do everything, is crippling, demoralizing, and frightening. I cried constantly. I tried to converse with people and couldn't because the only thing on my mind was what was about to come.

How do you face and be strong for the challenges that lie ahead when you want to stop the world and get off? I was not equipped.

How Do You Feel?
If your person received a terminal diagnosis, how did you cope with feelings of hopelessness? Did you find light at the end of the tunnel, and if so, how?

LONELY

No matter how many people surround you or how supportive they are, facing enormous life changes such as a sudden illness or an impending death can feel tremendously lonely. No two relationships are the same, so no two losses or tragedies can be the same either. Can anyone really understand what you are going through or how your devastation feels?

Cathy shares how she coped with loneliness.

Chapter 2

Cathy

We were walking up a snow-covered hill when I looked back and teased Gary about being so far behind me and our dog, Lily. This had happened before and he always said, "You have to keep up with the dog. I'm just out for a stroll." But this time he said, "I can't breathe."

I knew something was seriously wrong when he didn't put up his usual fight when I urged him to go to the doctor. At first, we thought it was pneumonia. They put him in the hospital for a week just as COVID lockdowns began, which meant that I couldn't visit him or advocate on his behalf. All I could do was sit at home, isolated, worried, and terribly afraid. I've never felt so alone.

When we talked on the phone, I could tell he was holding something back, so I started making deals with God. *Please, let him be okay and I'll…* My list of promises was long, but none of them worked. After that week in the hospital, he came home with a diagnosis of Mesothelioma, a fatal lung cancer. The doctor told him to put his affairs in order.

We both sat there, stunned, as we began to process the terrible news. So many thoughts ran through my head: *How bad will it get? Will I be strong enough for what lies ahead? How can I watch this strong, vital man slowly become less and less?*

But the most persistent question was a selfish one*: Can I survive without him?* We had been together for 28 years, and now our life together had been given an end date. The thought of him dying threatened my whole sense of being. Who would I be without Gary?

In the days that followed, Gary became more remote as he went through his own version of absorbing the shock. COVID was gathering steam and becoming more of a threat. We were isolated together, but we were each deeply alone in our own thoughts.

Gary had always been the one to comfort me and make me feel better.

Now, as the biggest threat of my life loomed ahead, I had to be the strong one and I couldn't turn to him for help.

How Do You Feel?
Did you feel lonely? What was that experience like for you?

ABANDONED

The prospect of losing a loved one can lead to feelings of abandonment. How can they leave me? What will I do?

Emily shares how she experienced feeling abandoned when her wife was diagnosed with cancer.

Emily

Veronica was in my life for twenty-two years, and over time we were able to have open and honest conversations in which we told each other literally everything. I remember being out of town at Veronica's niece's wedding when she came out of the shower and asked me to feel a lump she felt on the right side of her right breast. It was bigger than I anticipated, and definitely got me worried. She told me not to worry and to enjoy ourselves while we were there. I tried, but I remember thinking the worst thoughts as the possible reality started to sink in.

If it is cancer, will she have to go through treatment?

Will she have to do chemotherapy and radiation? Will she lose her hair?

Will she get really sick?

Will she die?

Chapter 2

Oh my god, she's going to leave me here all alone. I'm going to be abandoned again.

My heart sunk into my chest. I remember staring at Veronica while we were at the wedding and thinking about how much love I had for her and how much of an impact she'd had on my life.

What will I do if it's cancer? How can this be happening? Why her?

Veronica and I were total opposites and clearly, I'm the worrier of the two of us. She was her happy-go-lucky self, interacting with her family at the wedding like she always did. I was only able to capture beautiful memories with my camera that night.

After the wedding, we returned to our home community and the one appointment she made turned into many back-to-back appointments. They did a biopsy and sent away for the results. This was probably the longest wait in the whole entire world. When our doctor called her back to his office, we went together. Veronica was trying to be optimistic, being her usual joking self with the doctor, but she knew deep down that he was going to say, "it's cancer."

I remember the look on his face when he told us it wasn't good news. I immediately broke into tears. I couldn't contain myself. It was like it had been building up as she attended each appointment. Veronica was not the type of person to show very much emotion, but she was compassionate enough to console me as her spouse. Veronica was referred to the specialist in our neighbouring community who saw her a few days later.

How Do You Feel?
Did you experience feelings of abandonment? How did you cope?

Diagnosis: The Beginning of the End

EMPATHETIC

Empathy is an emotion that can help ease the pain of losing a loved one. When you put yourself in another person's shoes — or the shoes of those closest to them, if that isn't you — you can see things from a different perspective. Sometimes, the act of going outside of yourself helps you manage the more difficult emotions.

Carole recounts feeling empathy when she found out her close friend was losing her husband.

Carole

An unexpected call came from my good friend Sue. Her husband Dan (who was being treated for cancer) was now terminal. Momentarily stunned into silence, I quickly regained my composure and tried to put myself in her shoes. I had this realization that their solid bond was now on the path to being broken — and how absolutely devastating that would be.

Sue and Dan were a couple who defined *togetherness*. They met on the first day of university, married shortly after, and never spent a night apart for the next 45 years. They were playful, totally devoted to each other, and definitely 'glass half full' folk.

Putting myself in her shoes was a daunting proposition. The thought I kept to myself was: *how on earth will she cope?* Never the leader, always the follower, Sue had become totally dependent on Dan throughout their years together. It wasn't in her character to take charge — from balancing a cheque book to organizing daily spending and even planning vacations and trips. It was always Dan. I didn't blurt out any hint of these concerns. Instead, I calmly and quietly reassured her repeatedly, with as much heartfelt empathy as I could muster, that "I'm here for you, no matter what" while we sobbed together on the phone.

Chapter 2

Sue appeared to be in a state of shock herself, frequently struggling to express what had recently transpired with Dan's battle.

"I really wish I could make this cancer disappear," I recall stating. "What can I do to help you stay strong through this? Dan will be less anxious if he knows you have my support. I'll help you. I'll be with you. Please lean on me."

My words seemed to bring a degree of comfort to Sue. I promised her that I was available to fly out and stay with them at a moment's notice. She wasn't going to face this challenge alone. When a friendship is as long and deep as ours — we'd faced ups and downs, became parents and grandparents, and shared our most important family times — that friendship somehow transforms into family, and as family we were bound together for life. Friends became 'sisters from another mother' and Sue was that person for me. I knew that just my presence would take a tiny chip off the corner of their anxiety. I could help in the house for sure, but mostly I would be there to hug her tight, wipe her tears and be a sister for her.

How Do You Feel?

Write about how empathy for your loved one and for yourself showed up.

LOVE

Love is the most powerful emotion we experience as human beings. Its presence — or lack — is at the root of all the other emotions, from sadness to anger to joy. We wouldn't feel so sad or angry if we didn't love so fiercely, but nor would we experience the heights of joy.

Diagnosis: The Beginning of the End

Dave L.'s wife suffered for years from chronic pain. Dave shares the love he felt for Annie as together they navigated towards her MAID.

Dave L.

For Annie, there was no terminal diagnosis, no point in time that marked a tipping point from life to death. 'Death not foreseeable' was a phrase that brought despair, not hope. It was only three or four years after we'd met and fallen in love that Annie began to experience pain and fatigue. Her research turned up two names which matched the symptoms she had — chronic fatigue and fibromyalgia, names the specialist assured us meant nothing and were not a diagnosis.

But without a diagnosis, there could be no disease, and for Annie, that diagnosis was not confirmed for two more years. By then, we were caught up in an endless round of medical appointments resulting in drug prescriptions that brought severe side effects and little to no relief. Advice and therapy appointments only made Annie's symptoms worse. Concerned about the strain her illness might have on our relationship, she offered to end her life. For me, this was not an option and throughout the rest of our life together, the more she suffered, the closer we became. Forced to give up her work as a massage therapist and unwilling to waste what precious energy she had on a medical system that wasn't helping, Annie took charge of her own treatment, researching and finding treatments and specialists willing to listen and work with her.

By this time, I was her main support, taking charge of the household chores, so Annie was free to do what she could manage, which was often no more than walking the dog in the early morning. Although I would not fully understand it for many years, our love and the deep connection we shared made light work of the increased workload. I was still working a high-

69

pressure job, getting up at 5:30 in the morning to do yoga and meditate before the day began, and often getting to bed at 11:00 at night.

With the trajectory of her illness finally clear, Annie shared with me that when she reached her limit, she would seek to kill herself. By the time I retired a few years later, we had settled into a partnership based on love and mutual support that would carry us through to her final breath. Caregiving for us was not a one-sided relationship. Annie looked after me every bit as much as I looked after her, perhaps even more so. I continue to receive her support from the place she still occupies in my heart.

How Do You Feel?
Do you recall feeling love at the beginning of your person's journey? How did love show up, and to whom was it directed?

Diagnosis: The Beginning of the End

WHAT'S YOUR STORY?

If your loved one has just received a diagnosis that might lead them to consider MAID, then some of the stories in this chapter might be relatable to you and others might not feel like they represent your experience. If you are further along your journey in supporting a loved one through MAID, you will probably relate to many or all of these stories.

Listed below are each of the emotions presented by our storytellers. Consider which ones resonate with you and then use them to help you explore and honour your own emotions, knowing that they may be different from those expressed by our storytellers.

- Denial
- Shocked
- Confused
- Fearful
- Apprehensive
- Helpless
- Discouraged

- Angry
- Betrayed
- Sadness
- Hopeless
- Lonely
- Abandoned
- Empathetic
- Love

How Do You Feel?

Which emotions and stories resonate with you?

Which emotions do not resonate with you?

What emotions have you felt that were not included?

Has anything that you've felt during your journey surprised you?

What does this mean for you now?

CHAPTER 3 -

DISCOVERING MAID

No one ever told me that grief felt so much like fear. — C. S. Lewis

MAID became legal in Canada in 2016. At the time of writing this book (2022/23), it was still a relatively new option for people wishing to end their life because of a terminal diagnosis or irreversible decline. The very newness of MAID can make finding information about it a challenge. Also, MAID was legalized by federal order, but healthcare is implemented provincially and delivered locally, which means that access to MAID differs depending on the health region in which you live.

In this stage of the MAID journey, our storytellers share how they felt when MAID came into their lives. For many, this happened by necessity when their loved one decided MAID was an option they wanted to pursue. Others learned about MAID as a political idea before it became legal in Canada in 2016, and long before finding out that their loved one qualified.

How does it feel to discover that taking control over how you end your life is not only a possibility but a legal right? How does it feel when your loved one wants to consider ending their life with MAID? Many storytellers felt gratitude, exhilaration, compassion, and relief when they discovered that their loved one had options. However, emotions can shift and change day by day and hour by hour, and no two storyteller's journeys are the same. It can be much easier to imagine feeling supportive and hopeful of a hypothetical than it is to be challenged by the reality. Some people may not agree with MAID. Intense sadness, shock, anger, fear, and denial are also common. Your feelings and beliefs about MAID will impact how you experience your person's MAID journey.

In Chapter 3, each of our storytellers share one of the many emotions they experienced when their person decided to end their life with medical assistance.

OPTIMISTIC

Changes in the laws relating to MAID over the past few years have, for many, been a source of great optimism. Finally, relief is at hand. Their loved one can choose to end their suffering and face the light at the end of the tunnel on their own terms.

Carole shares why finding out about MAID made her feel optimistic should she get to the point in her life when she says "I don't want to be here."

Carole

When I first heard about MAID many years ago, I must admit that I was rather overjoyed to hear it was on the path to becoming a reality in Canada. Previously, I'd been aware of procedures available in Holland and Switzerland, but now this was potentially something feasible on my home turf!

Of course, my optimism was self-centered because at that point I didn't know anyone personally who could benefit from the option of MAID, but it certainly gave ME hope. This option could alleviate my own fears. While I'm not particularly afraid of death, the prospect of a slow death causes me immense angst. Despite my zealous approach to living a healthy life, I know that no one can cheat the aging process or the onset of a host of medical conditions.

I've spent time with loved ones in nursing homes and witnessed the 'barely living' existence they endured. It was distressing for them and for me because I wasn't able to help in any meaningful way.

"I don't want to be here" were the last words I heard from my uncle before the drugs kept him pain free but virtually unresponsive for a few more weeks before he passed. I know with 100% certainty that he'd have welcomed the opportunity to have a MAID procedure many months prior to his death. And he is one of many I have encountered in similar situations. Each person expressed the thought that they'd 'had enough.' While we all desire to live a long and healthy life, when that is no longer possible, I believe it's humane to offer people the choice to opt out.

I'm optimistic about the path forward with MAID. Knowing it is an option brings such a feeling of relief, comfort, and reassurance.

How Do You Feel?
How does knowing that MAID exists as an option make you feel?

PASSIONATE

MAID in Canada has been the subject of much passionate debate over the years, which has resulted in our legal right for MAID. One storyteller shares why she feels that MAID should be a choice that each of us is entitled to make for ourselves.

Anonymous

My husband and I had always believed that unnecessary suffering was, well, unnecessary. We both knew that all kinds of illegal euthanasia was going on in the world and wondered why we could compassionately put our pets' misery to an end but couldn't offer that same compassion to our human loved ones. Wealthy people could always go to an exclusive clinic somewhere in Europe, but that option wasn't available to most of us. So, we watched and followed the debates in Canada on medically assisted death.

Up until MAID became available in 2016, the only options for those suffering a lingering death were to commit suicide or refuse treatment. We had witnessed such choices made by loved ones. We had determined that we wouldn't allow that to happen to either of us should the time come. Neither of us believed there was any nobility in enduring a prolonged, agonizing, but inevitable death.

And so, we rejoiced when MAID became legal in Canada. This meant that we could choose, if the time ever came, and that we didn't need to linger in pain. I have always feared dying a piece at a time like my father did because of complications from Type 1 diabetes. I am also a diabetic and had vowed I wouldn't die as he had. My husband's family also had cases where the only way to end prolonged suffering was to refuse further treatment. Once MAID became a legal option in Canada, my husband had frank discussions about MAID with our family physician long before

75

there was any expectation that we would be discussing it as an actual option.

I was, and remain, an advocate of medical assistance in dying. I passionately feel that everyone has the right to determine for themselves when they want to die. For some, choosing death over certain suffering is considered suicide, a word that still evokes an ugly stigma. To those people my response is, fine, then don't have medically assisted death but do NOT tell anyone else that they should be banned from making that choice. It is an individual choice.

The right for everyone to choose or not choose MAID remains their own. I continue to advocate for an individual's right to choose medical assistance in dying and continue to lobby for broader terms, such as allowing for advanced requests. Why is that important? Because there is no one to advocate for me if the time comes that I may require MAID.

How Do You Feel?
Do you have strong feelings about MAID?

HOPEFUL

Hope is defined as 'cherishing a desire with anticipation.' For some storytellers, learning that MAID was an option for their loved one, especially after they had suffered for months or years, brought a tremendous feeling of hope.

Dave L. shares how learning that his wife was finally able to legally end her life made both of them hopeful that an end to her pain was finally within her grasp.

Discovering MAID

Dave L.

It's ironic that Annie would have died much sooner, by her own hand, had MAID not been so tantalizingly close. We were talking seriously about her final days when the first MAID legislation was written into law. What held Annie back was not that she was afraid to die, but the fact that partners and spouses who supported those who took their own lives were being vigorously prosecuted and sentenced to prison terms. If Annie took matters into her own hands, she would have to do so alone, to protect me.

By then, Annie had developed multiple medical conditions, each of which caused her more suffering and the sum of which might eventually be considered terminal. We hoped that if things just got a little bit worse, she would qualify for MAID and not have to end her suffering alone.

By the time the MAID legislation passed in 2016, we had been together for 25 years; Annie had been sick for 21 years and I had been retired for nine.

Despite Annie's pain and fatigue, and her constant battle with side effects from the drugs, our life could have been considered almost idyllic. The routine we settled into supported us both. We had help with the housework, and a young friend who had become like a daughter to Annie came in a couple of times a week so Annie and she could do girl stuff. There was a lot of joy, and once the new legislation came in, a lot of hope that the final relief Annie sought was not too far away.

The 'foreseeable death' requirement of the original MAID legislation had kept Annie from applying right away, but by 2019, her suffering was becoming intolerable, and she felt confident that she'd qualify for MAID. Although we knew her application might be refused, we were both hopeful that Annie would be allowed to decide when she was ready to die — and that we'd be able to be together in her final moments.

Chapter 3

How Do You Feel?
Has learning about MAID brought you feelings of hope?

RELIEVED

If a loved one has been suffering for a long time, news that MAID may be an option can sometimes be accompanied by feelings of relief. But along with relief may also come feelings of guilt. How can death be a relief? But for many it is, and for our storytellers, respecting a loved one's desire to end their life with MAID becomes an act of love.

Elizabeth, who was faced with losing both her parents, shares how her feelings of relief for the parent who could have MAID clashed with feelings of sorrow for the other parent who could not.

Elizabeth

I am embarrassed to admit that I don't really know when I first heard that Mom was looking into the MAID process. It feels like it should be one of those moments in which you remember exactly where you were and what you were doing, but I don't.

Mom had been to the oncologist and had been given the news that no one wants to hear. There was nothing further they would be able to do to help her. There were no more chemo drugs to try, no other options.

My mother did not want to die in a hospital bed hooked up to a bunch of monitors and IV lines. She started looking into MAID in the summer of 2016. My parents told my siblings and me about Mom's decision to investigate the MAID process and the basic steps required for approval. My parents lived in Victoria, British

Columbia, where the providers were much more advanced and 'trail blazing' compared to those in Ontario where I lived.

I relied for the most part on the information our parents shared about MAID because, in those days, very little information was readily available.

Dad had been suffering chronic pain for at least two years by this point, and he wondered if he'd be eligible for MAID at the same time as Mom. He wanted to die with her, hand in hand. I absolutely fell apart thinking about losing both of my parents at the same time; I just wasn't ready. In reality, you are never ready, no matter the circumstances.

Our family learned that Mom would be eligible for MAID, but that Dad would not. What a mixed set of emotions! Dad would still be with us, but now we would be entering a new reality where we were, in fact, going to lose Mom. I felt a huge wave of relief wash over me for Mom, but sorrow for Dad. He was devastated that the current law would not allow him to die because his death was not reasonably foreseeable.

How Do You Feel?

Did you feel relieved when you discovered that your person qualified for MAID? Were your feelings of relief mixed up with other feelings?

Chapter 3

EXHILARATED

Discovering that, finally, your loved one can choose to end their suffering on their terms, can be exhilarating. Finally, the pain can give way to peace, the suffering to stillness.

Dave B. shares how he and his wife Annie felt when they discovered that Annie qualified for MAID.

Dave B.

Annie's diagnosis of Stage 4 colon cancer came in the middle of April 2019. After an initial assurance from her surgeon, following emergency surgery a month earlier, that it was *not* cancer, we learned that our years together now had an end in sight. We were both numbed and then gloomy about the prognosis. Annie needed to have chemotherapy as soon as it could be arranged, but she had an open studio tour at the beginning of July that she wanted to prepare for first. (She did, and the show was a great success.) Her life was all about her art, and she was not willing to start any chemotherapy that might affect her ability to work.

I felt like we were on autopilot for the next month, going through the motions of dealing with everything. She mysteriously lost control of her voice and was unable to eat. Could these new ailments be a result of ALS, as one of the home care nurses first suggested?

After the cancer diagnosis, Annie was placed in the palliative care program. "This doesn't mean you're about to die; it's to make you as comfortable as possible right now," we were assured. At the beginning of August, we had a visit from one of the local hospice workers. In the middle of the conversation about palliative care and the hospice movement, she said, "And you know you'll be eligible for MAID."

Annie and I looked at each other and smiled with wonder. What joyous news! We were aware of MAID, but we didn't know anyone who had chosen it and we'd never considered MAID as a possibility for Annie. We both saw the news now as a positive way in which to avoid a painful death, and best of all, a way for Annie to finally have some control over her life, even though it meant ending it.

After many months of fear about the inexorable advance of the cancer, and the great, worrying unknowns of possible ALS, discovering that MAID was available was positively exhilarating.

How Do You Feel?

Can you relate to this feeling of exhilaration in learning that your loved one has a choice?

APPRECIATIVE

When a loved one decides to end their life with MAID, it's sometimes helpful to take a step back from the inevitable sorrow and fear to appreciate their courage. We have been conditioned all our lives to choose life at all costs. Immense courage is required to make a contrary choice.

As a health care worker who routinely witnessed the suffering of patients whose deaths were unnecessarily prolonged, Shannon began to appreciate the gift her friend was giving herself and her loved ones by choosing to die on her own terms.

Shannon

It was the week prior to Wendy's chosen date. I was working at the hospital one night and a code blue was called. It was early in the morning and the distinct alarm rang out overhead and

Chapter 3

instantly flooded my body with adrenaline. My heart thumped through my chest as I arrived at the patient's bedside and saw he was in obvious distress. A man in his sixties with a very similar diagnosis to Wendy's. My heart sank when I saw that the report ended with 'no code status on file.' I couldn't believe it.

How had we allowed this to happen? We were going to use everything medicine had to offer to keep him alive. *Did he understand what that would mean? Is that really what he would have chosen if he did?*

Everything our team was about to do to sustain this man's life flashed before me. We did chest compressions that snapped his ribs. We placed a breathing tube down his throat, which caused him to vomit. We inserted IVs and gave numerous medications and fluids. We did tests and discussed which actions to take next, all while we continued to be his heartbeat and his breath. Nausea intensified in me as the length of our efforts continued without the return of a heartbeat. His pupils were fixed and dilated, which is never a positive sign, but still we continued. It was at this point that I let myself hope that this human soul had passed. I clung to the belief that he was unable to feel our efforts—physically, emotionally and spiritually.

He spent several days on life support, intubated and mechanically ventilated with all sorts of medications running through his bloodstream to maintain his life but also to keep him comfortable. His family had to witness his slow death.

When I left the hospital after that shift, the November air was misty, cool, and damp. It felt fresh and smelled of recent rain. I took a few deep breaths and let gratitude wash over me. *Wendy wasn't going to suffer like that.*

I felt an immense sense of appreciation for Wendy's courage to intentionally face what was right in front of her. She was consciously considering how she wanted to *live* the rest of her life and choosing how she wanted to *die*. I felt a wave of relief in knowing that all her loved ones, including me, would be spared the traumatic experience that my patient's family was having to endure.

A massive shift was occurring in my own perception of what was truly significant in life and in death.

And isn't that comfort? Love? Warmth? Security? Peace?

How Do You Feel?

What, if anything, do you appreciate about this process, this option called MAID?

GRATEFUL

No one wants to watch their loved one suffer from the debilitating effects of a disease or condition for which there is no positive prognosis. So, when death is inevitable, finding out that MAID is an option can come as a great relief. Feelings of gratitude replace the fear of having to watch your loved one spend their last days in pain.

Andrée shares how grateful she felt when the doctor was supportive of MAID for her daughter.

Andrée

Kim had been through chemotherapy, radiation, a stem cell transplant that gave us an extra four years, and one blood transfusion after another. She was at the point where nothing was working anymore. She had been in and out of the hospital frequently during the previous months, and now we were out of treatment options. Her oncologist suggested she may only have three to six months left to live.

I remember asking him about Medical Assistance in Dying (MAID), knowing that not all doctors feel comfortable or in favour of it. I was so grateful when he told us that he did support MAID. It was a relief to know she had that option. I didn't want Kim suffering longer than she already had or end up hooked up to a respirator. I wanted her to die peacefully.

As a family, we had watched both my parents and Kim's father die of cancer. At the end of his life, we sat with her dad in the hospital waiting for him to go. It was so sad. He was unconscious, lying there emaciated, looking nothing like the man we knew, hooked up to a respirator as we waited for the end. As much as I didn't want Kim to die, I did not want her to die like that.

I was grateful MAID was there for her. She was in so much pain with sores all over her body and she was getting weaker by the day. She needed a wheelchair to get around, and the medication was never enough to control her pain. I felt relieved knowing that at least Kim would have a choice when the time was right for her.

How Do You Feel?
How did you feel when you discovered that MAID could be an option for your loved one? If you felt grateful, how did it help you along the MAID journey?

CONTROL

Regaining a sense of control is a common and understandable reaction to news that MAID may be available for a loved one. A long illness or devastating diagnosis spins us out of control where fear, anger, and dread swirl and mingle.

Geneviève and her husband, who had been diagnosed with dementia, regained control of their future when they discovered that MAID could be an option. Only then were they able to have the difficult conversations about death.

Geneviève

My husband and I first talked about MAID the night he came home and told me that he was experiencing issues with his brain. He just came out and said, "And you know what I will want to do!"

My mind was already reeling, and I felt disoriented. I needed to catch up to the conversation, not move well into it. I was just not ready to talk about death, let alone assisted death. We had to find out what was ahead of us first.

Unfortunately, he was right. He had dementia. So, talk about death we did. It was never something that we'd talked about much before. Life was meant for living, not planning for death. These conversations were very uncomfortable, surreal even. We were in our fifties. Why were we talking about death? I was falling into an abyss with no lifeline.

'What did we believe in? What did he want to do? What did we want to do? What were his wishes? Were our affairs in order? Where were we at financially?'

Most importantly, how was he going to go about it, especially because he wanted to die in Canada. No dementia patient, to our knowledge, had received MAID before. The only way to regain control of everything we were losing was to have these incredibly difficult discussions.

Our conversations around death were numerous, sad, and scary. There were times when I needed to run away and scream. I had to leave the house and go for a walk. I couldn't handle it. How could this be happening? I was frantically searching for answers, guiding hands, anything. At the same time, our talks about death were very empowering, and we were able to get to know each other in ways we never thought possible. In a hopeless situation, these conversations gave us a sense of power, of regaining control. The disease was progressing unchecked, but we could decide when and how it would end. I guess these conversations were our answers, after all. They gave me the strength to stand beside my husband and our children in his decision. It was an ounce of control, and it turned out to be all that I needed.

How Do You Feel?

How does the level of control you have in this experience right now make you feel?

CONFUSED

Finding out that MAID is an option for your loved one can also lead to intense feelings of confusion. *Should they consider it? What if they do? How will I cope? Why is this happening to us? What will people think?* Confusion saps strength and numbs action.

Nikki shares the confusion she felt when she switched from being her father's caretaker to her father's MAID advocate.

Discovering MAID

Nikki

Well, this is confusing. We are really shifting gears here. I just spent the last eight years working with doctors and specialists to do everything I could to keep my dad healthy, and now, I'm doing everything in my power to help him regain some control and choose his own ending by accessing MAID. *Wasn't I supposed to keep doing everything possible to keep him alive and well? Isn't that what Western medicine has taught me?* Here I now was, fighting and advocating for my father's ability to choose to end his life on his terms.

How will I manage it all? I'm so burnt out from the constant stress of caretaking, of days living on the edge, bleary-eyed, just going through the motions of getting things done. I go to bed every single night wondering if I will wake up to learn he has died alone in his apartment, having fallen again, with nobody there to help.

I forced him to get Lifeline, but, like so many other systems I tried to implement, he rejected wearing the necklace that could potentially save his life. So, I bring in the DNR form, but he won't sign it. I guess he figures I'm fine with finding him again on the bedroom floor covered in his blood and urine after spending the night there because he couldn't get up. What's a little more trauma?

I dread the idea of having to answer to friends and family who do not know and understand the depth of his suffering. The constant nagging dread of these conversations makes me feel as though the entire contents of my abdomen are dropping right out of me. They will not understand why he has made this choice. I'm running on empty. I'm living in the RED, always on high alert. Always on call. Always tired. So tired. I can't bear the thought of what his siblings will think of me. *Are they going to blame me? Will I be judged for advocating on his behalf? Will I be made to feel guilt and shame because of my actions?*

Yup. Nobody actually believes he will go through with it. This enrages me. *Who makes this decision lightly?*

How Do You Feel?

How did confusion affect you when you discovered that your loved one was eligible for MAID?

IRRITATED

Sometimes, it's not easy to admit having certain feelings, particularly those considered 'negative.' But we are only human, and feeling irritated and annoyed with a loved one considering MAID may feel preferable to actually listening and empathizing.

Carol just wanted her mother to stop talking about MAID because talking about it made it far too real and maybe even likely.

Carol

For at least six months prior to my mother's death, when she was suffering from acute anxiety, she frequently declared that she wanted to jump off a bridge. She didn't respond to any of the many medical interventions we tried and increasingly declared that she wanted a medically assisted death. I felt irritated just about every time she brought up the subject.

"No, Mom. You can't do that."

"But the lady down the hall just had it."

"Yes, but she had a terminal illness. You don't, and so you can't have MAID. "

I had no idea how wrong I was.

I just wished more than anything that Mom would stop talking about ending her life with MAID. *Why talk about something you can't have?* I felt irritated because I didn't think someone like my mom would be eligible for MAID. Sometimes, I let my irritation show and spoke sharply to her. All I wanted to do was help her get better, to stop the frantic phone calls, to stop all this talk about jumping off bridges. I was focused on keeping her alive and well, so the last thing I wanted to do was talk about her dying.

Dying was for sick people, and Mom wasn't sick. Not really. The irritation tightened my jaw and stabbed at my voice. Instead of acknowledging her pain, I tried to erase it. I wanted her old self back so badly that I refused to soften my impatience. If I could just get annoyed enough, tell her often enough that she was going to get better, all this talk about dying would go away.

The day I checked Mom into the long-term care unit, I mentioned to the manager that my mother kept asking about MAID. I added that, of course, I knew she couldn't have it because she didn't have a terminal diagnosis from a disease such as cancer.

"Actually," the manager said, "She probably does qualify for MAID. The law just changed a few months ago to allow people to choose MAID even if death isn't immediately foreseeable. Several of our residents have chosen that option."

What? No way. Now what? I knew without an ounce of doubt that if I told Mom she might qualify for MAID, she'd want to do it.

My irritation gave way to a feeling of intense dread.

How Do You Feel?
Did you feel irritated when your loved one expressed a wish for MAID?

Chapter 3

SHOCKED

Finding out about MAID, particularly in relation to the possible death of your loved one, can come as a terrible shock. What does MAID even mean? Is it really an option? Why? How?

Robin and Emily share how shock affected them when faced with the prospect of a MAID death for their loved one.

Robin

I learned about MAID in an email. More specifically, I learned that particular acronym in an email.

My dad dropped it into a message to my siblings and me as though it was something perfectly normal to be discussing. It was a year after he went on to oxygen full time and a month after he had moved into a Seniors' lodge.

"The palliative care nurse left me with some information about MAID," he said, "and I think it's time to start looking into it."

"What's MAID?" I asked.

I'm normally the sort who would Google these things, but for some reason I didn't.

The answer came the next day. It was a Thursday morning, and I was working from home, thank goodness.

"It stands for Medically Assisted Death," my dad said. "It's something I'm considering for the future."

The feeling when I read those words was shock — complete and utter shock. A month earlier, he'd been living at home with my mom and still puttering around the house. He'd now moved into a place where he could get support, but it was not a care home. He wasn't that ill, or so I thought. So why was he talking about dying? It didn't make sense to me how an assisted death could be part of the conversation.

I didn't even finish reading the email. I just sat there, stunned. Everything else faded away. I forgot about work and whatever had been on my to-do list for the day. A thousand things went through my head at that moment.

What? A medically assisted death? I guess I knew that was legal, but I didn't even have that on my radar. He wants to die? Where did this come from?

I found the courage to continue reading the email.

"I think I've still got quite a while before any of this might be necessary. The medical people keep asking me about my heart, so maybe I'll be lucky and have a heart attack in my sleep."

What? WHAT?! I was so shocked I felt like I couldn't even process what he was saying.

I texted a friend to tell her because it was too big to stay within me. I couldn't believe I was actually typing those words.

"My dad is considering a medically assisted death."

I don't know what I expected or wanted her to say. What was there to say? I was already crying and practically hyperventilating. I was home alone and just needed someone to be with me in that moment.

The thoughts continued.

Is this real? What does that even mean? I'm going to lose my dad.

Emily

While Veronica was sick, one of her friends was diagnosed with brain cancer, and she was in and out of hospital for about a year. When we went to visit her in the hospital, she and Veronica had a heart-to-heart about how painful having cancer was.

I felt so helpless sitting there listening to Veronica speaking her truth to someone who understood her, someone who was going

91

through what she was going through. Their cancers were literally growing from the inside out and taking over their bodies. This was an eye opener for me because I was her spouse, but yet I was oblivious to her pain. Yes, I saw it in her eyes and heard it in her voice, but I didn't get it. Veronica and her friend both had terminal cancer. I did not.

About a week after we went to visit, Veronica told me that her friend had passed away with MAID. She explained that a date had been set, and that she was 'put to sleep.' That's all we knew about MAID at the time, and we didn't talk about it again. Little did I know that this concept was brewing in Veronica's mind. She always talked about wanting to die in her sleep. I never put two and two together until this moment. Was she telling me, but in her own way?

About a year after her friend's MAID procedure, Veronica brought up MAID for the first time when the home care nurse came to visit us. It was a huge shock; I remember sitting there in my rocking chair beside her, tears streaming down my face. *What … how can she be thinking of this? This will mean she is choosing to die,* I thought as my chest tightened.

The nurse couldn't give us much information, so I looked MAID up on the Internet. I showed Veronica the application form and told her she would need two witnesses and two doctors to sign off on it. Veronica looked over the papers and she immediately started naming who she wanted to tell about her decision.

I knew she was serious. I didn't want to fight with her. I didn't want to be that person who was being selfish and ask her not to. I loved her too much to try to convince her to change her mind. I had to be there for her. Veronica asked me to get the papers printed and signed to take with us to the doctor's office a few days later. My heart was beating out of my chest. I didn't know what else to do but be beside her.

How Do You Feel?
Were you shocked when you learned about MAID? How did that
feel? How did you act?

DENIAL

When a loved one decides they want MAID, we may
acknowledge their wishes while feeling absolutely positive they'll
never be put into practice. How could they? Our loved one is
going to get better, right? Feelings of denial are common.

Brittney shares how she supported her mother's decision to have
MAID while at the same time denying its likelihood.

Brittney

My mom had decided right from the very beginning of her
diagnosis that if 'things got bad' she wanted to go through with
MAID. She made it very clear that she did not want to suffer. As a
personal support worker, she had witnessed many patients with a
low quality of life and she did not want that…no way, no how.

We were all very supportive of her decision — it was up to her, and
no one was going to stop her, but no one actually thought it
would come down to that. I remember reading an email she sent
to the whole family informing us about her next doctor's
appointment. She ended the email with " … and if things get bad, I
want MAID." I felt ill when I read that last part, instant denial,
because that was never going to happen. She was never going to
get that bad, right? My beautiful mom was healthy, strong and
would beat this. She was the strongest woman I knew! It was just
a little cancer on her jaw, not on her liver or lungs. The very last
thing on my mind was having to say goodbye to her. It seemed so

Chapter 3

damn unfair. MAID was not something I wanted to think about, let alone have to do.

As time went by, I thought more about MAID because the emails would carry on, with the ending once again reminding us of her wishes. I told a close friend about MAID and that my mom wanted to go ahead with it if it came down to it. I told him in a joking way, because it was just crazy talk to me, putting the cart before the horse. He said, "Well, she just wants to have everything ready and prepared, just in case." *Okay, I guess so,* I thought to myself with that nervous pain in my stomach, *but there won't be a just in case!*

I was in denial for years. My mom would have a nine-hour surgery to remove the cancer from her jaw, complete six gruelling weeks of radiation and ta-da, she would be cured, right? She could talk about MAID all she wanted, but in my mind, she would not need it.

Throughout the next few years, Mom's emails after appointments and scans always mentioned MAID. I felt scared and almost angry. *Why does she keep mentioning this? Is her cancer back/getting worse? Does she not have any hope? Or does she just want to make sure we are all on the same page with her wishes?* It got to the point where I did not like hearing the word MAID because who wants to think about death? Especially the upcoming, planned death of a loved one? It was just bizarre. I needed my mom more than I would ever know.

How Do You Feel?
How has denial played a role in your experience?

FEARFUL

Fear of the unknown is a human trait, and what can be more unknown than death? When your loved one decides to die, they have chosen a journey that requires them to conquer their fear of death. But for those of us left behind, conquering this fear is hugely challenging. We're not ready to go yet, so how can they be?

For Cathy, fear of what lay ahead, both before and after her husband's death, preoccupied her even as she supported her husband's decision.

Cathy

It didn't surprise me when Gary chose MAID. Over the years, we had talked about how ironic and inhumane it was that society would end the pain and suffering of an animal but not a human. When the legislation allowing MAID was passed, we both saw it as progress.

I accepted that it was his choice to make, and I agreed to it. In fact, I felt relief and gratitude that we would be in control at the end. I couldn't stand the thought of him enduring prolonged suffering. I also didn't know if I was up to being the caretaker to the very end. I had never had to deal with that level of adversity in my life. Yes, I had gone through the trauma of divorce, but otherwise my life had been a relatively smooth sail.

Would I fail him when he needed me the most? I was terrified of letting him down; this man who had always been the strong one would depend on me ... maybe for his very life. I lay awake at night, panicking over what lay ahead. My mind raced, my stomach churned, and silent tears dripped on my pillow until I'd finally give up and take a sleeping pill, so I'd be able to function the next day.

I felt inadequate and alone. And then Gary decided on MAID.

But wait a minute. Even though I was grateful, I couldn't take in the reality of what it was that we were accepting. Yes, I was relieved that we wouldn't have to go through those last dreadful days, but then the truth of what we were talking about hit me and I furiously wondered *how can this possibly be happening?*

Part of me hated MAID. The very team that was so helpful and kind would — can I say it? — kill him. I wanted to protect Gary, to tell them to get the hell away and never come back. *How could they do this job, then go home to their families and their normal lives?*

I knew it wasn't logical to feel that way because Gary's illness was going to kill him one way or another. But layered within my gratitude and acceptance of MAID was always the terrible fear of how it would end.

How Do You Feel?

Fear is one of the most debilitating and yet understandable emotions with relation to death. What role did fear play in your MAID journey?

ANGRY

Anger can take many forms in relation to the MAID journey. Sometimes, anger may be directed at fate — How can this be happening? Why me? Why them? At other times, anger erupts as a result of tangible things such as the quality of health care or the slowness of bureaucracy.

Bobbie shares how her devastation about her husband's decision to have MAID was bound up with her anger that poor hospital care had hastened that decision.

Discovering MAID

Bobbie

Twenty-three years into living with Parkinson's, Bob woke up more confused than normal and was admitted into the hospital for what we thought would be a short visit. Unfortunately, he caught an infection and ended up staying for five long weeks. I'm convinced that the poor care he received over this hospital stay led to him choosing MAID sooner than he needed to.

His hospital stay was during the height of COVID, so he had to be isolated, which also meant he had no television. His sight didn't allow him to use an iPad, and people continually turned off his radio. I wasn't able to convince anyone that he should be transferred to a larger hospital that was better equipped to deal with his Parkinson's and his unknown infection. All I could do was visit him and keep him company, so he wasn't so alone. The most dreadful part for Bob was being strapped into a wheelchair for long hours and having to not just wear a diaper but being told to just use his diaper instead of the toilet. My husband was a gentle man who always was able to find the best in people, but when the nurse who forced him to wear diapers was on duty, he did nothing but complain. He HATED that wheelchair, and he hated the diapers. He wanted to walk, but the physiotherapist only came for a short time a few days a week. Although he was weak, he'd always been a very fit man and was positive he could walk.

It was spring in Vancouver and unusually warm for April, so I was allowed to push him in his wheelchair outside. We both loved 'escaping' that room. We would go for as long as I could manage the heavy chair and my 200 lb husband.

One day when I came to take him outside, he had shredded his diaper all over the room. This was really out of character for my gentle husband. I had never seen him so upset and completely depressed. He was tired of being told to just pee in his diaper. He had developed a diaper rash, and he felt he had lost all his dignity. I walked out of his room and just stared at the nurse at the desk, afraid to speak, I was so frustrated and angry. I worried that if I said anything, it would just make things worse for him. And that is when he started to talk seriously about MAID.

We went to meet his sister at a little park. She had prepared his favourite egg salad sandwiches. Bob was obviously agitated, and as soon as we got to the park, he asked me to help him get MAID. His sister held his hand, and I cried. I was stunned and in shock. I truly felt that if he had received better care in the hospital, he would not have had the diaper issue, and with some rehab, he would have been able to walk, and I could have managed him at home for a while longer.

I sobbed all the way home. I cried as hard as I ever had before. I screamed in the car. The reality was hitting me, and I felt like my heart was being torn in two. How in the hell had this happened? I know we'd talked about MAID in calm times, but this was something so different. This was so real. I was having trouble breathing and could feel my head pounding as I drove home, away from the dreadful hospital to scream alone.

I didn't know how I would manage to support him when all I wanted was for him to come home.

How Do You Feel?

Did you feel angry when you learned about your loved one's decision to have MAID? Explore how feelings of anger affected you.

DISORIENTED

Even if MAID has been talked about and planned for, the reality that it's actually going to happen can be tremendously disorienting. *I thought I had more time* is a common feeling.

Cynthia shares how disorientated she felt when she realized that her husband had only a very short time during which he would be able to choose MAID[1].

Cynthia

"A new tumor is growing aggressively in your left temporal lobe. Close to speech, memory and vision." The oncologist spoke quietly, trying to disguise the crack in her voice, unable to hide the tears in her eyes.

It's time reverberated off the walls in a deep, sombre voice.

Dread flooded my body. The air in the room tasted as thick and heavy as it felt. The conversation slowed to a freeze frame pace as I glanced through the fog to see if my husband was understanding what this meant. The progression was evidence that 'the chemo was not working.'

It's time.

We had just crossed my husband's line in the sand.

It's time.

He had always been adamant he didn't want more than the standard treatment.

It's time.

---

[1] The death of Cynthia's husband occurred before the Waiver of Final Consent became legal in 2020.

Chapter 3

No additional surgery, no new chemo, no clinical trials, nothing experimental.

It's time.

I shook my head. A ghostly hand ripped a fist full of pages off the imaginary calendar of my husband's life and threw them in the air. The 12 months that I had been terrified to live through — full of worries such as how to keep him safe in the winter, when to hire a caregiver, when to let others take our kids — were suddenly gone. I'd wanted to skip them countless times, but I had also been clinging to them.

It's time. No. No. No.

I was completely unprepared to face our plan.

The oncologist started talking again. "The new tumor's location means he could lose mental capacity quickly. If his intention is to access MAID, his window to legally consent is at risk. He needs to act soon."

It's time.

More pages blew off the calendar in my mind, floating through the air like snowflakes, close enough to touch, but impossible to catch.

It's time.

I was disoriented by the speed at which his life was shortening. I felt dizzy as I mentally calculated how long we would have left together? Six months? Three months? Two months? A week?

It's time.

I thought about our children, playing at summer camp nearby, blissfully unaware.

It's time.

I crumpled into my mom's arms in the waiting room, struggling to accept the shrinking timeline of my husband's life. I hated the thought of telling my kids that it was time for their father to access MAID. I imagined holding them while they too felt the excruciating pain of this tragedy we had all been expecting, yet were completely unprepared for.

How Do You Feel?

Do you recall feeling disoriented when you realized that your loved one was going to choose MAID? Take some time to write about feeling disoriented.

Chapter 3

WHAT'S YOUR STORY?

Did you just learn about MAID recently or have you known about MAID for a long time? Your level of knowledge about MAID may change how you feel and react when you learn of a loved one's choice to have medical assistance in dying. It's common to feel both surprised and upset and yet still supportive of a loved one's decision.

Listed below are each of the emotions presented as our storytellers found out about MAID. How many of them can you relate to, and which were the hardest for you to allow yourself to feel?

- Optimistic
- Passionate
- Hopeful
- Relieved
- Exhilarated
- Appreciative
- Grateful
- Control

- Confused
- Irritated
- Shocked
- Denial
- Fearful
- Angry
- Disoriented

How Do You Feel?

Which emotions and stories resonate with you?

Which emotions do not resonate with you?

What emotions did you feel that were not included?

Has anything that you've felt during your journey surprised you?

CHAPTER 4 -

GETTING APPROVED FOR MAID

What do we live for, if not to make life less difficult
for each other. — George Eliot

None of us wants to see our loved one suffer. MAID offers them and us a way out, but the path is strewn with many complex and conflicting emotions. Once a loved one has decided they want to die with medical assistance (MAID), the next step is to reach out to the medical community and find out how.

Who do we contact? How long do we wait? Who will decide? Where do we go? How will it all happen? What's the procedure? Will it be hard?

These are just some of the many questions asked by the people who are seeking MAID and those who support them. It's not uncommon for storytellers to find that the brunt of the practical work of procuring MAID falls on their shoulders. Paperwork, interviews, appointments, and bureaucracy take MAID from something vague that has only been talked about, to a more proximal reality. An event thought to be far in the future suddenly grows closer. At this point, a date may even be set.

Chapter 4

This chapter will not provide answers to the logistical questions of procuring MAID. Instead, you will find one story from each of our storytellers that highlights one of the many emotions they experienced during their involvement with the process of helping their person procure MAID.

APPRECIATED

Helping a loved one handle all the logistics associated with applying for and being approved for MAID can be time consuming and frustrating. When a loved one shows appreciation for our efforts to help them procure MAID, calmness and contentment may replace feelings of turmoil and concern. It can be a nice opportunity to help our loved one with an important decision.

Carol shares how her mother's appreciation for her help in procuring MAID kept her going and helped soothe the rough edges of her grief.

Carol

I feel incredibly lucky to have been the principal support for my mother during her last weeks. Mom was fading more and more each day and depended upon me to 'get MAID' for her. Her determination, along with her appreciation of my efforts, kept me focused and sane. I contacted the MAID people, set up the appointments, was present at one of them, and made the final phone call to set up 'the day.'

While part of me rebelled at these tasks, I was buoyed by my mother's constant appreciation. She made me feel like an angel for helping her go the way she wanted instead of the monster I sometimes judged myself as for helping my mother die. During the last weeks, she often said, "I'm so lucky to have you as my daughter." That heartfelt appreciation really helped me overcome the fear that I wasn't doing enough for her because I couldn't make her better.

My permission was very important to her. I remember her asking me if I was okay with her choosing MAID. I wanted to say *No, of course not. Stay alive!* But I didn't, because I knew in my heart that Mom really wanted to make this choice for herself. She didn't want to die alone in the care home. She wanted to die with me by her side, and I wanted to be there with her. Never was there a moment when I wasn't committed to that intention. It was my one constant, my way to truly thank her for all she'd given me.

Her constant appreciation buoyed me and kept me moving forward.

How Do You Feel?

Did your loved one appreciate your efforts in helping them through the MAID process? How did this affect you, either positively or negatively?

GRATEFUL

Knowing that an end to your loved one's suffering is in sight can bring you incredible feelings of gratitude. Something practical is finally being done to move the process forward. Your loved one is getting closer to the peace they are so desperately seeking.

Dave B. and Cathy share their feelings of gratitude.

Dave B.

We had received so much bad news. Annie had emergency surgery and then four weeks later received a diagnosis of Stage 4 colon cancer. For months, Annie's eating and speech had steadily deteriorated. She felt she was losing control of her life, and I felt helpless because I couldn't do anything to slow it down or stop it. I couldn't protect her from what was happening.

After the diagnosis, the doctor changed Annie's status to palliative. This led to a visit from a hospice volunteer who brought us the news that MAID was available to Annie, and that she would likely qualify after she was assessed. At last, Annie might be granted control over how she would die. Knowing in the abstract that MAID is legal in Canada and that many people had already had it was one thing, but accepting and believing that Annie's personal ordeal could soon end in a relatively peaceful way at the time of her choosing turned out to be a huge relief.

At times—not too often, thankfully—I crashed. I ranted to her in the vein of 'what about me?' At these times, I felt guilty and inadequate. I had only one job in those 17 months and that was to care for Annie, and I sometimes felt miserable that I wasn't doing a good enough job. Mostly, however, I felt a deep sense of gratitude throughout the entire process towards all the people involved in Annie's journey. I was grateful to the weekly home care nurses who visited us, the workers at Inspire Health in Victoria, and Annie's new general practitioner who finally, gently delivered her from her pain.

I think we both felt gratitude. Annie was happy that she had control over her end, and I was happy that her suffering would soon be over. I'm also grateful that we live on Vancouver Island in British Columbia, where everyone we encountered on our voyage was kind and supportive toward Annie. I will miss her forever.

Cathy

How am I going to do this on my own? was my panicked thought as I ended my call to the family doctor's office. I had phoned to ask for medication to help Gary get some sleep, which the pain in his back was preventing. The doctor was there, but he couldn't be bothered to talk to me, relaying to his nurse that we should go to Emergency.

What the hell? How could the doctor be so cold and unresponsive when he knew we were dealing with a fatal illness? How could the task of keeping Gary comfortable and alive for as long as possible fall completely to me?

And the even more pressing question was, *Am I up to it?*

That's when I contacted the Home and Community Care and Support Services and arranged to have an intake person sent to our house. That person turned out to be Ram, a registered nurse and one of the kindest, gentlest people I've ever met. He was with us from that day to the day Gary decided he could take no more. Also with us was Cindy, the Nurse Practitioner who administered MAID eleven months later.

The process of procuring MAID went smoothly for us. I've heard stories about bureaucratic nightmares, meddling relatives and religious objections, but we had none of that. When I think of MAID, I think of Ram and Cindy and the team we formed to help the bravest man I've ever known meet the toughest challenge of his life.

One of the most unnerving things for me as caregiver was that, as time went on, the cocktail of medicines Gary was taking progressed with his illness. Because of this constant change, I was terrified that I'd get confused and give him the wrong medicine or dose, which could be fatal. But Ram and Cindy were always there to consult with, to explain the changes when I was confused and to outline the adverse reactions I needed to watch for. And every time I walked them to the door after a visit, they turned to me and asked how I was doing. They would look at me with kindness and concern and gently remind me to take care of myself.

At first, they visited every two weeks for a few hours. As a team, we dealt with each escalating crisis as it arose — from horribly

Chapter 4

swollen legs, to difficulty breathing, to constantly increasing weakness and pain. Toward the end, Ram and Cindy came every day. Their calm and competent presence kept me from panicking as Gary's symptoms and illness grew worse and worse.

And as much as they helped Gary through his terrible ordeal, they supported and befriended me through mine. I was never alone as I'd worried about being in the beginning because Ram and Cindy were there when we needed them. I'll never be able to thank them enough.

How Do You Feel?

Did feelings of gratitude arise as you navigated the MAID procurement process?

IMPATIENT

When your loved one has suffered for a long time and no longer even looks like themselves, a natural reaction is impatience to have their ordeal end. On the one hand, setting a date can feel callous, but on the other hand, it can be the kindest thing to do for both you and your loved one.

Daimhin shares how she longed to find closure so that healing could begin.

Daimhin

We were all sitting in the living room. I felt like I had a pit in my stomach the size of a watermelon. Dad's condition had drastically declined, and he was already beyond the point that he wanted to avoid. It was hard to look at him; he was a weaker version of himself and seldom laughed anymore. I felt like I had already lost my dad.

Unfortunately, we were stuck in the summer vacation of a couple of doctors and were unable to get Dad's second assessment done as quickly as we wanted. As a family, we were discussing logistics. Yes, logistics of when my dad would die. Picking the day he would die made my mouth dry and my face hot.

This is so fucked up.

We ruled out the first week of September because it was my sister's birthday, so someone suggested the second week. The pit in my stomach grew, twisted and raged as I sat there.

"I don't want to start my last year of university late," I said. "We need to do it earlier."

How can I think that? I want to move up my dad's death because it's more convenient for me?

Dad's disease had already taken so much from me, and I didn't want it to take anything more. We all needed to get this awful chapter behind us and start the healing process. The man sitting in front of me was a shell of my dad and prolonging his death just dragged out the pain, anger and heartbreak of having someone you love fade away before your eyes.

I don't know whose suffering I wanted to end more — his or mine.

But no matter what, the outcome would be the same; my dad was going to be dead soon, and my heart was breaking.

How Do You Feel?
When have you felt most impatient during this process?

Chapter 4

EXCITED

Caring for a loved one is exhausting and all-consuming. Your life is no longer your own. Trips are cancelled, plans put on hold, hobbies go by the wayside. The idea of having time for yourself becomes a dream. In the midst of the agony of waiting for your loved one's MAID, it's natural to sometimes imagine a life without constraints.

An anonymous storyteller shares how she sometimes felt excited by the prospect of one day having time to do as she pleased.

Anonymous

Even though we have approval for MAID, he has yet to choose a date. As I sit through endless treatments, visits to emergency, infections and other setbacks, I wonder about my future. *What will my life be like? Will I be afraid to be alone in the house? How will I fill my time? Will I be a burden to our children?* The reality is, barring some unforeseen event, I am going to outlive my spouse. And there will be a life for me that is not being his caregiver. Sometimes I let my mind drift, imagining 'the tomorrows.' I indulge in positive thoughts of a future alone, after he is gone. I get excited for what might be, like a teenager moving away from home. My time will be my own again. I can make plans without the constant need to cancel them. Perhaps I can travel again. I could take on a volunteer position and actually commit to it. I imagine coffee with girlfriends, dinner dates and theatre outings. The idea of tanning on a warm beach or relaxing with a soothing massage is enticing. Reading a whole book without interruption!

Thinking about my future alone is exciting. I'm looking forward to being able to do things that I enjoy, have conversations that stimulate me, and motivate me to get involved. Watching my husband deteriorate slowly is lonely, tiring and overwhelming. Thinking about what I have to look forward to, gives me the strength to carry on through this hell.

How Do You Feel?
Have you felt excited during this process? How and why?

NUMB

Feeling numb can be both a blessing and a curse as you support your loved one through MAID. On the one hand, it's easier to jump through all the MAID hoops — the paperwork, the appointments, the visits — when you can put all your emotions on hold. Numbness helps get things done. On the other hand, you may feel guilty when you keep your grief at bay.

Elizabeth shares how she felt numb while witnessing both her parents choose their MAID dates.

Elizabeth

I will probably remember this moment forever. My mother had been approved for MAID in the early fall of 2016. I was sitting with my parents in their living room, and Mom announced that she needed to see 'the calendar' with all the medical appointments, social events, visits from friends, and major events in the lives of their three children.

Mom and Dad sat side by side while they looked at the calendar and talked about choosing a date for Mom to have MAID. It was completely surreal, and I think I probably went numb. It felt like they were making a plan to go grocery shopping or setting a lunch date. For something that was so incredibly impactful, they seemed so very calm.

I struggled to keep my composure, not wanting to fall apart in front of them, but my head was spinning. Can I get back to them? (I was visiting them in BC from Ontario, and they were setting a date that was about three weeks away.) Would my two siblings be able to make it in time? Would I be strong enough to witness and support them? My brain was in turmoil.

Although I wanted to support them both, my mind was screaming *NO! This can't be happening already.* Dad had also investigated the process for himself, but he'd been told he didn't qualify. He was quite unhappy about that, and I was worried that he would try to find another provider that would approve him. Facing the thought of losing them both at the same time was unbearable. My body and brain started to shut down.

When my father was approved for MAID in 2021, he requested that the process be done almost immediately, although he did agree to wait three or four days so that my siblings and his three grandchildren could get out to see him. Time stood still.

I had four days to help my father and make that time count.

How Do You Feel?
What role did numbness play for you as you navigated getting approved for MAID? What emotions do you think you were experiencing beneath this numbness?

Getting Approved for MAID

Helpless and Anxious

Watching your loved one suffer, sometimes for years, takes a tremendous toll on your emotions and can lead to you feeling both helpless and anxious. Why can't you make them better? Why did this happen? What can you do?

Brittney shares how helpless she felt when, finally, there was an end in sight for her mother's battle with cancer; Robin shares how she felt anxious due to a lack of information about MAID; and Bobbie shares the anxiety she felt leading up to her husband finally being approved for MAID.

Brittney

As the years went on, so did my mom's cancer battle—six years filled with radiation, two surgeries, check ups, scans, blood work, nurse visits, etc. After the second surgery on her jaw, my mom never quite healed the way we were expecting and hoping. It was hard for her to eat because of the pain, although she never admitted it. She continued to lose weight and just never got back to 'normal.'

Eventually, the pain in her jaw got worse, and she knew the cancer had returned. Eating anything other than liquids was a struggle for her. Even the smoothies and soups I made were not an option anymore. This made me feel so useless, so damn helpless. *What could I do to help her?* I was just waiting for my mom to write (she had lost her ability to talk) on her marker board, "Okay, I'm ready to die" as I watched her waste away, losing weight, unable to take the dogs out, not wanting us to make a fuss. There was nothing I, nor anyone, could do to alleviate her pain, give her the ability to talk or eat, or make all the shit go away.

I just wanted things to go back to normal. *How was this happening to MY mom?* It became a horrible waiting game, knowing that my

113

mom's death was imminent and all we could do was basically sit around and wait.

I remember one day when I went over to my mom and stepdad's place. Mom was having issues with the morphine pump; it was making strange noises and morphine is not something you want to mess with. My mom was a little panicked and my heart broke because she wasn't able to fully communicate with my stepdad. They were pressing buttons on the little machine that was tucked in the fanny pack she wore around her waist. I wanted to help, but I couldn't. They usually relied on me to 'fix' things like cell phone or internet issues, things that parents often need help with. I could not fix my mom's problems, and it made me feel nauseous and numb.

How the hell was I supposed to eat and enjoy an evening out after witnessing my dying mom struggling with her pain pump? How the hell was I going to get through the next few days or months waiting for my mom to give the green light on her death? How the hell was I going to live the rest of my life without her?

Robin

I wasn't involved in my dad's process to apply, be assessed or approved for MAID. My brother helped him with that, which let me be blissfully ignorant. That seemed like a fine thing until we knew the date and I recognized how much I had pushed the very idea of MAID off my radar. It was at that point that I realized that I didn't know anything about it.

When my brother called to tell me that our dad was going ahead with MAID in a week's time, it launched me into a couple of days of being fuelled by adrenaline. My hands shook as I sat at my kitchen table googling MAID and finding very little useful information. I wanted to know how it worked and what to expect on the day. I wanted to know what I should tell my kids.

Getting Approved for MAID

The provincial website had one page of very clinical information aimed at the patient. It didn't answer any of my questions. I gave up, disheartened.

The adrenaline went away to be replaced by the knot in my right shoulder that shows up when I'm stressed or anxious. It just sat there like a golf ball right next to my shoulder blade, reminding me every time I leaned back in my chair or lay down in bed that something horrible was happening.

I'm the sort of person who likes to know what to expect, but I went through that last week without having any of the answers that might have made the process just a tiny bit easier. I didn't know how MAID worked, and I didn't know what would happen on the day. I blundered my way through an explanation to my kids, feeling sad and disappointed that there wasn't more information available to family members.

I never did find out what I needed to know. I just nervously went along, and it wasn't until after Dad died that I found some sources of information and comfort that helped me process the choice my dad had made and what it meant for the rest of us.

Bobbie

I could tell by the look on the ward nurse's face that she didn't feel that Bob was mentally well enough to be approved for MAID. I felt physically sick. I was so mad at myself for leaving this so long. It terrified me to think that Bob might not get his wish to die on his own terms, after 23 years of suffering with Parkinson's Disease.

We waited all weekend, which seemed like the longest weekend of our lives, to speak with the doctor and the social worker. They looked like aliens, dressed in their full COVID gear, which I hated. I noticed the looks that they gave each other while asking Bob questions. It was like they were shouting their negative thoughts.

Chapter 4

Please look at my husband, not me, and stop these signals with each other, I screamed in my head. I was so scared; worried that this wasn't going to work out in Bob's favour. They didn't show one ounce of compassion. We were exhausted when they left and had no idea if they had given their approval.

The next appointment was a long and difficult phone call with Bob's family doctor, who didn't really believe in MAID. We turned on the speakerphone and held hands so tightly I had bruises the next day. Once again, I was screaming inside with frustration at the doctor's questions. I could see how hard this was for Bob.

We had to wait six days to hear that Bob's request for MAID had been approved. During that time, I was terrified, scared, and heartbroken. I kept wondering *how can I be helping my adored husband die?* I didn't want him to die, to be gone, but this was my job, as his wife; to support him 100%. He didn't want to go into long-term care, and I couldn't take care of him at home anymore. The last few years had been so hard, and I was so tired of being his caregiver. I knew he was choosing MAID as much for me as for himself, but I would get confused and wonder *what if he is making this choice for me, and I am only supporting his choice because I want to put him first?*

It made my head and my heart hurt to try to sort it out. Would long-term care really be so bad? At least he would still be here.

When Bob found out he had been approved for MAID, the change in him was unbelievable. He was so relaxed and relieved that I knew he was finished with this journey. But there was no joy in my heart. It was breaking.

How Do You Feel?

How did helplessness and anxiety manifest for you during this portion of the MAID journey? How did the ways in which you expressed your anxiety affect your relationship with your loved one?

CONFUSED

Getting answers to all the questions when you want them and finding help navigating MAID can be challenging and confusing. Although improvements are being made on provincial health websites to point people to the correct information, it can still be difficult.

Geneviève shares her feelings of confusion while helping her husband apply for MAID.

Geneviève

The whole process of applying for MAID—the many checks and balances—left me feeling dazed and like we were walking on a tightrope. It is not a common path, so we were not well prepared for the intensity of it. In all honesty, during this entire journey, I was totally out of my element. No wonder I was feeling so confused and insecure.

What happens when....? How do I....? What does it mean....? How do I handle...?

There was an endless barrage of questions, both about the process and about myself. Yet I still had to be strong for my husband and my children. I tried to imagine every conversation that was going to occur with my friends and with the medical professionals. I tried to understand what my husband was going through—his

117

determination and his deep disappointment that this was happening to him.

I tried to imagine what life would be like without him. *How was I going to face the world alone?* This question in particular made me extremely anxious, nervous and frightened. My head, my heart and my mind were in a serious tailspin, as though I'd entered a maze and was continuously taking wrong turns. I felt shaky and unsure.

And at the same time, there was also a slight sense of relief that my husband would no longer be in mental anguish, that he could still have an ounce of control, and that I would see an end to this ordeal.

How Do You Feel?

Can you relate to feel confused while trying to help your loved one apply for MAID?

FEARFUL

Our innate fear of death makes MAID very difficult to understand. How can our loved one want to die? Aren't they frightened of what's ahead? Life is known; death is not. We as storytellers must deal not only with the fear of our own death, but our fear of a life without our loved one.

Emily shares her feelings of fear as she witnessed her wife starting on her MAID journey.

Emily

Veronica was not one to complain about anything, especially when it came to her pain. She didn't want anyone to worry about her. But as her spouse, I saw the pain in her face and heard the sounds she made when she was hurting. Veronica had lung cancer, and sometimes the pain would be so intense it would take her breath away. Near the end of her life, she needed to use oxygen from time to time to help her catch her breath. This was not something she wanted to do, but she didn't have a choice. With her quality of life changing and her not being able to get around without assistance, Veronica knew what she needed and didn't see the point of living a few extra months and being miserable.

When we talked about MAID, she knew what was at stake, but she also knew what was best for her. MAID was an opportunity to take away her pain and suffering and also mine. Veronica wasn't scared. With the cancer she had, she wanted to prepare us as best she could. She wanted to make sure that everything was in order before she died. I tried my best not to show her how scary this was for me.

My heart pounded out of my chest every time I tried to envision a life without her. I had lived with her for over half my life and had never lived alone. Even when I went away to school, I lived in a room and board arrangement. I never had to cook or clean for myself; I always had someone. I was afraid that I wouldn't be able to handle living on my own. This was compounded by the fact that I didn't have my mother for guidance. I had lost her to cancer seven months before Veronica died. They had both been by my side to give me love and support in everything I did in life.

Imagining a life without them crushed me inside, producing an emptiness I can't explain. It felt so surreal and numbing to know that soon my two best friends in this world would be dead.

Chapter 4

How Do You Feel?

Did you experience fear during this stage of the MAID process? Was it fear of life without your loved one or fear of your own death (or both)?

PANICKED

How can we not feel panic when witnessing a loved one's suffering and knowing their death is near? Panic can debilitate us, leave us gasping for air and unsure where to turn. Panic comes from fear of the unknown, and nothing in life is so unknown as death.

Jane shares how panic slowly turned to anger after her husband signed the papers applying for MAID.

Jane

It was done, the MAID papers were signed shortly after Christmas. No date was chosen, but there was so much to do and prepare for. First, we had to tell my husband's adult children. How would they react? As we set up the family meeting, my stomach was in knots. I wanted to be strong for my husband while he told them of his decision. I was worried about how they would react, but to my relief, they were very supportive of his wish.

The fact that I was not the mother of his children created a lot of unknowns for me and contributed to my state of constant panic. So many questions — *How will we get help through this process? What about telling friends and extended family? What will I need to prepare for on The Day?*

120

I wasn't able to eat much, and my nervous energy kept me busy. Days slid into months and no decision was made, although talk was constant when my husband would have a bad day.

A year passed, and life became an emotional roller coaster. The constant vacillation between "I'm calling the MAID provider" and "I'm not ready yet" turned my panic into anger. His health was rapidly deteriorating. I was his caregiver, and I was wearing out. I wished he would just 'shit or get off the pot.' I was not used to expressing anger and at first, I didn't realise it was anger that I was feeling.

I would find myself crying at night or in the car. I had physical feelings I couldn't control; my whole body would start to shake, and I would run outside and sit on the cliff overlooking the lake until I could catch my breath. Normally, I was a calm and easy-going person, but the uncertainty of daily life left me wound up tighter than a drum. I would yell at our pets for no reason at all. I felt guilty for yelling and guilty for wishing he would make up his mind and get it over with.

How Do You Feel?
Did you worry about telling people of your loved one's choice to have MAID?

GUILTY

Our loved ones may want to shield us from the pain they know we'll feel when they pass. Sometimes, they even choose to prolong their own suffering rather than inflict more suffering on us by dying. This situation can lead to feelings of guilt as we struggle to reconcile wanting them to stay alive with protecting them from more suffering.

Chapter 4

Andrée shares how she felt guilty when she discovered why her daughter held off requesting MAID.

Andrée

I watched Kim struggle to get herself to yet another appointment at the hospital. She was so weak, it broke my heart to watch her get dressed, go down the stairs of the house, and step in and out of the car. I felt every painful step she took, as if it were my own. After her appointment, I reminded her that she had a choice and we discussed MAID. She told me that she was ready; it was time. She also admitted that she had been holding off requesting MAID to protect me, to not hurt me. I had been by her side these past 10 years through all the ups and downs of her treatments. I had been her cheerleader. She didn't want me to think she was giving up.

I felt so guilty thinking about her enduring more pain than necessary all in an effort to protect me. She didn't want to be another loss in my life or add to my pain. My daughter was worried that I would be hurt by her choice. I had been trying so hard to stay positive and strong for her, so that she didn't have to worry about my pain on top of her own.

Of course, I didn't want Kim to die. She was only 31. This is not the way life is supposed to go. I am the mother; I am supposed to die first. But I also didn't want her to keep suffering. I didn't know what was worse, imagining the pain I would feel when my daughter died, or watching her suffer every day, some days telling me she couldn't go on.

I thought she knew I would support her decision to choose MAID. I was the one who had asked her doctor if he would support her when the time came for MAID. I wish I had known that she needed me to let her know sooner that I was okay with her choice. I told her I would support her no matter what. It was a hard conversation, and we cried all the way home. By the time I dropped her off at home, she knew I would stand by her and help her on this last journey.

How Do You Feel?
Did you experience feelings of guilt about your loved one choosing MAID? Take some time to think about what role guilt may have played during this stage of the MAID journey.

RESENTFUL

Unexpected emotions can sometimes be the most challenging to deal with during the MAID process. Sadness, anger, and certainly grief are expected, but what happens when we're blindsided by feelings that don't seem logical or are unexpected? Every emotion during this journey is valid — the good, the bad, the expected, and the surprising.

For Cynthia, her feelings of resentment towards the MAID assessors who interviewed her husband as part of the MAID application process took her by surprise.

Cynthia

My husband's first MAID assessor was a gentle, quiet man, and the second was a sympathetic and kind young woman. They both came to our home, about two weeks apart, and spent close to 90 minutes patiently listening to my husband make his case for why he wanted to die. I think they were surprised when he walked independently into the living room and waved hello. He didn't look sick or frail or dying, and he wasn't experiencing any pain.

In spite of their thoughtful questions and empathetic demeanours, I still resented these gatekeepers for taking up our precious time while they assessed my husband's fitness to choose to end his life.

Chapter 4

"Does he understand his diagnosis and his treatment options? Does he comprehend what he is asking for and why?" I held my husband's hand and smiled, masking my clenched teeth and burning cheeks. I hated that he was being forced, through garbled words and strained speech, to justify his choice, to seek approval from these strangers.

His frustration was evident as he searched his tumour-riddled brain for the words he wanted to say. His eyes pleaded with me to help him, to speak for him. He regularly relied on me to be his voice. I sensed the assessor scrutinizing my motives as she glanced between my husband and me, weighing my words against his expressions, looking for his physical acknowledgement. I wanted to be grateful for her patience, for the existence of MAID, for her dedication to the right to choose and to patients like my husband, but all I could feel was resentment. I wished she understood what those 90 minutes meant to us, that the conversation was my husband's only one that day because it would leave his mind and body exhausted from the effort of searching for words and answers to satisfy our country's legal requirements.

Bile rose in my throat. I wanted her to hurry up, to stop being so patient and thorough. I wanted her to leave her glass of water half finished, to skip the unsolicited recommendation against our kids' participation in his death, and to leave my living room. Quickly.

During these interrogations, his decision, his choice, hardly felt like it was truly 'HIS.' It surprised me to feel so resentful towards these well-meaning helpers.

How Do You Feel?
Were you surprised by any of the emotions that you felt as your loved one applied for MAID?

Ashamed

We often feel that we should be strong for our loved one who has chosen MAID, but sometimes, it's not so easy to hold in the tears. We might feel shame for 'giving in,' but such moments are all part of the process to be acknowledged and then moved on from so we can truly 'be there' for our loved one.

Shannon shares how shame consumed her after breaking down when her friend asked her to be with her when she died.

Shannon

I remember showing up one morning with a pumpkin-spiced latte for Wendy's sister. I was told that Wendy had endured another awful night and, as I entered her home, I felt a sombre weight pressing down on me, like I was diving into a bottomless lake. The pressure surrounded my entire being, compressed my chest and threatened to suffocate me. I sat next to Wendy, and she said, "I picked a date. It's two weeks from today. I'd really love for you to be there."

My face contorted in a pathetic attempt to hold back tears, and then I gave in and sobbed and grieved for my friend in that moment, right in front of her. The pressure released, and I came back up for air. And then shame gripped me. How could I be so selfish? How could I lose control? How could I let Wendy see my sadness? My weakness? I was terrified of my own emotions and totally unable to predict when and where they would burst out of me. I figured I'd have time to sort through these feelings after Wendy was gone. At that moment, I wanted to be the rock she could lean on, and I didn't want to impose any of my needs on her. I was so ill-prepared for these cyclical tsunamis of grief that occurred during the two weeks before she passed.

Chapter 4

How Do You Feel?
Were you able to express your feelings to your loved one? Did you feel you had to hold back? What did that feel like?

DISMAYED

When MAID finally becomes real, perhaps after months or years of waiting, you may feel dismay. Your loved one is getting what *they* want, but what about you? How do you really feel about the prospect of losing your loved one?

Nikki shares the dismay she felt when her father finally qualified for MAID.

Nikki

He's been approved. It took nine months, but he's been approved. He is the best version of himself I have witnessed in years — bright, happy, sharp. It is startling, yet a nice surprise to see him in such fine form. It brings me momentary peace. This is certainly what he wants. My heart fills with hope and warmth. We have done it! But it hasn't been easy.

Remembering how hard the journey was makes my body seize again and steals my moment of joy. We had to wait for his health to worsen before his application was approved. He literally had to look half-dead before he was given access to what he so desired. There were hurdles, hard conversations, sleepless nights, tears, yells, hugs … and everything in between. And now, the hardest part began. The 14-day countdown.

Day 14, I wake thinking that Dad will be dead in 14 days. He calls me several times a day for the next two weeks. *When is the doctor coming?* I reassure him it will all be over soon.

126

13 more days until Dad dies. "It's ok, Dad, he's coming. We are still on track. Just be patient."

12 more days until Dad dies. I ask if he wants to talk to his friends or siblings. "No."

11 more days until Dad dies. *Holy shit. This is actually going to happen.* Disbelief.

10 days until Dad dies. I take my girls to visit him. I have to hold my little girl in his arms because he is too scared and frail to hold her himself. We are taking pictures — the last pictures with my dad that we will ever take as a family. Deep sadness.

9 days until Dad dies. I am now drinking to numb my pain. I don't even know what it is I'm really feeling — a mixture of pain, anxiety, impatience, anger, resentment, fear, annoyance, and relief. And so, I numb myself because it is all too much. My daughter is sick. My dog has hurt his back. My husband is working crazy hours.

My girlfriend arrives for two days from out of town. I try to pretend like everything is normal. But it's 8 days until MY DAD DIES. I try to ask him about funeral arrangements. He refuses to engage in this conversation with me. I don't want to upset him further, but what the fuck am I supposed to do? *How is this falling in my lap? Why is this becoming my decision?* I don't want to bury him. I leave the conversation alone.

7 days until Dad is dead. One week. Dad will be DEAD in one week.

6 days until Dad dies. My mother calls me. She's falling apart. I welcome her to ground zero in a not-so-warm way. I hold back the tears and my urge to yell at her because I'm at Whole Foods picking up food for my dad and trying to stay on top of my own household duties. *Where have you been all year? Keep your shit together because I only have time and energy for me and Dad.*

Chapter 4

5 days until Dad is dead. It's snowing. It makes me happy and is somehow comforting. Like it's blanketing my wounds.

4 days until Dad is dead. My brother promises to come stay with my dad for the next 3 nights.

3 days until Dad is dead. My brother doesn't show up. *FUCK HIM!*

2 days until Dad is dead. *Keep it together, Nikki. We are almost there.*

1 day until Dad is dead. I reassure him one last time that yes, tomorrow is the day. Tomorrow is the day we will all be free of this particular hell we have been living in.

How Do You Feel?
Do you remember the moment that your loved one chose a date for MAID? How did you feel?

DESPAIR

MAID applications can be refused, and this can lead to feelings of despair for both you and your loved one. It's terribly disheartening to make the heart-wrenching decision to apply for MAID only to be turned down.

Dave L. shares how he felt when his wife Annie's application for MAID was refused.

Dave L.

When Annie's application for MAID was refused on the 'no foreseeable death' provision, we were in despair. We knew there was the possibility of being turned down for this reason, but when there was no response from the MAID assessor for a couple of weeks, we began to hope there was a chance.

Annie felt sadness and anger that the system required the applicant to be in the process of dying before they would consider offering relief from the suffering. I was concerned and worried that Annie would take the ending of her life into her own hands without telling me. It was a possibility we had talked about many times and, given the aggressive prosecution of spouses who had actively supported their partner's suicide, Annie had determined that I was to have absolutely no part in what she planned.

In all the years of supporting Annie through her illness and suffering, the prospect of being cut out of the process at the ending of her journey was devastating. I understood, of course, and the rational part of me couldn't find fault with her reasoning, but there was little that was rational about this situation, or about the thought of the solitary death of my beloved wife. Although she stuck it out for another 20 months, she did eventually try to take her own life in my absence. That, for me, was the hardest place I have ever been in. Even though her attempt was unsuccessful — or perhaps because it was unsuccessful — I felt such deep grief. It was only caring for Annie and convincing her to apply for MAID again that brought me any relief.

How Do You Feel?
Did you experience having a MAID application turned down? How did that feel for you and your loved one? How did it feel when the application was finally accepted (if it was)?

Chapter 4

WHAT'S YOUR STORY?

If you are the closest person to your loved one, you've likely been asked to help find information, sign forms, make calls or arrange appointments for your loved one to have MAID. Depending on where you live, how much you already know, and how quickly your loved one wants to die, this role can be more or less taxing on you and your emotions.

Listed below are each of the emotions presented by our storytellers as they helped their loved ones navigate the process to procure MAID.

- Appreciated
- Grateful
- Numb
- Helpless
- Anxious
- Confused
- Fearful

- Panicked
- Resentful
- Guilty
- Ashamed
- Dismayed
- Despair

How Do You Feel?

Which emotions and stories resonate with you?

Which emotions do not resonate with you?

What emotions did you feel that were not included?

Has anything that you've felt during your journey surprised you?

CHAPTER 5 -

SAYING GOODBYE

There is a sacredness in tears. They are not the mark of weakness, but of power. They speak more eloquently than ten thousand tongues. They are the messengers of overwhelming grief, of deep contrition, and of unspeakable love. -
Washington Irving

Even when someone we love is very ill, we can never know exactly when they will die, nor when we are saying goodbye for the last time. But this is not the case when your loved one chooses MAID. You actually *do* know when goodbye is really goodbye. The date, the time, and the place are set, and everything is arranged and in order. Your loved one has made their decision and given their permission. They've signed the forms, met with the caregivers, agreed to the logistics, and made peace with their decision.

But what about you, the survivor? What's it like to help your loved one choose a date and arrange the details of their last moments? How do you interact when you know exactly when they are going to die? How do you say goodbye?

In Chapter 5, our storytellers share some of the many emotions they experienced in the days and moments immediately

Chapter 5

preceding MAID during which they were coming to grips with how to say goodbye to their loved one.

GRATEFUL

Witnessing a loved one decide to end their life on their own terms can lead to feelings of gratitude, even happiness. They are giving themselves the gift of control over how and when they wish to leave this earth and including you in it. It can be a particularly positive experience to witness families and friends gather and share and celebrate together.

Daimhin shares her experience during the 'Fun'eral' given for her father in the weeks prior to his passing.

Daimhin

The 'Fun'eral' was a whole weekend affair. People from all walks of my dad's life, from all across Canada and the US, came together for one last hurrah and the chance to say goodbye to their brother, cousin, nephew, uncle, and friend. Our neighbours and friends opened their homes to strangers. In most cases, the only thing they had in common was that my dad had touched and enriched their lives. Although it was during the toughest time of my life, that weekend is one of my best memories. It was the light in the darkness. I was surrounded by people who all loved my dad and wanted to celebrate him and his amazing life.

The weekend was full of laughter, games, music, food, dancing, and also goodbyes, tears and heartbreak, but the former outweighed the latter. With every conversation he had or person he spoke with, I felt the weight and tension lifting little by little off my shoulders. It was the weight of worry and fear that people wouldn't get a chance to say goodbye, but also the weight that I would feel alone after he was gone.

But how could I possibly be alone when I had all these amazing people in my life? Watching my dad say goodbye to the people who loved him was one of the hardest things I have ever witnessed. He spent individual moments with each person, and they shared memories, laughs and lots of tears, but the main thing they shared was love.

How Do You Feel?

Did you feel grateful for the opportunity to say goodbye to your loved one? What were those last few weeks and days like?

ACCEPTANCE

Acceptance of a loved one's death can lead to a sense of peace and release. You've come to terms with what's about to happen and you can focus on cherishing the time you spend with your loved one.

Dave L. shares his experience during the last weeks of his wife Annie's life.

Dave L.

The two months between Annie's approval for MAID and her death were profound for both of us. We felt so much joy when her application was approved. It was like a weight had been lifted from both our shoulders. There was no sense of anticipation of her upcoming death. For us, death had become an ordinary part of life, not something to look forward to and certainly not something to fear. Annie's pain increased, but strangely, so did her energy. It sounds like an oxymoron to say that she found a new lease on life, but that's what it was.

Chapter 5

Those two months were crammed with sorting through boxes of letters and photographs and packing up bits and pieces to send to friends and relatives and hauling them off to the UPS store. We shared stories about the people she'd known, connected with friends, and heard their gratitude for the support she'd offered them throughout their lives. From the moment Annie had been approved, we both felt a sense of peace, and in this sharing, any separation between us dissolved, establishing a connection that was to transcend her death.

On her last full day, Annie woke up early, with no pain and lots of energy. It was a beautiful autumn morning. She had breakfast and announced that she'd like to go downstairs and sit on the back deck. For years, she'd only been able to sit outside for an hour or two at most before the pain drew her back to her bed, but on that day, we ate lunch together, fed the squirrels, and talked and read poetry for most of the afternoon. She still had no pain and lots of energy, which made it easy for me in the late afternoon to take her back upstairs to bed, where we continued talking and laughing into the evening.

As night fell, I kept an eye out for the harvest moon that had been part of the reason for her choosing this particular day. It was a cloudy night, but eventually the moon became visible through breaks in the clouds and Annie moved into her window seat to watch its passage. Once it had disappeared behind the neighbour's house, well past 10:30 pm, I helped her back to bed.

That day had been the best day of our relationship, and I slept well.

Saying Goodbye

How Do You Feel?

Did/do you feel accepting of your loved one's decision? Were you able to make positive memories of saying goodbye?

If your loved one is still alive, do you have an idea of how you would like to say goodbye?

RELIEVED

After many months or years of taking care of your loved one, knowing the end is finally near can come as a relief. Although we are aware that sadness will inevitably follow, we can't help feeling relieved that not only our loved one's suffering, but our own, is coming to an end. Feeling relieved is often rather difficult to speak about because it can cause us to feel guilty or selfish. It's important to recognize that relief is an incredibly normal emotion to feel during the grieving process.

Dave B. shares how he felt relieved when the date for his wife's medically assisted death was set, and Andrée shares how relieved she felt when MAID allowed her independent, strong-willed daughter to be in control of how she wanted to die.

Dave B.

Annie's last few days were especially hard on both of us. Her life had shrunk with her loss of abilities, but she was heroic to me, in fully living those days, creating her artwork in paint and fabric, spending as much time as she could in the garden. She was inspiring. And so, it was a surprise when the 'day of' came so unexpectedly.

Two days before she died, she felt pains similar to those she felt before her emergency surgery 17 months earlier. She couldn't sleep those last couple of nights. We slept in the same bed, and I

Chapter 5

was now impatient with her leaving the light on and getting in and out of bed so often. I felt truly drained after caring for her for so many months. My own life had vanished. I felt like a robot, like I was a passive observer of my life. I was sad, of course, for the state of her life and for the things she had lost, such as her ability to speak or to eat properly. And so, in some ways, I felt relieved when she decided to proceed with her medically assisted death and announced that it was time.

No more sleepless nights. No more making phone calls she couldn't make herself. No more caregiving. No thought at this point of what would follow.

Andrée

The time had come to say goodbye. Finally, Kim would stop being in so much pain. The nurses had to use burn bandages to treat the sores and lesions that were literally eating away at her body, and her medications were being increased almost daily.

It was so hard to see my beautiful daughter suffering and not be able to do anything for her. I felt relieved that Kim had access to MAID, a way to end her pain. It gave her a sense of control over her life that I could tell brought her comfort.

From the day she was born, Kim was very independent. She always had a mind of her own, but this cancer had taken that from her. I missed my strong-willed, determined girl. As a mother, it was awful to watch her cry in pain and not be able to hold her. The sores on her body were so extensive that I couldn't touch her. I could only watch her suffer and struggle as the pain took over.

I was proud to see Kim choosing to go on her own terms, choosing where to die and who to invite. It was a relief to see a small piece of the independent daughter I had always known.

Saying Goodbye

How Do You Feel?

Did you feel relief once a date had been set for your loved ones medically assisted death? Write about your feelings of relief and how easy or difficult it is to acknowledge this emotion.

Determined

The last days before a loved one leaves us are often chock-full of activity — practical matters to attend to, family and friends to meet, arrangements to be made. How do we make the most meaningful memories? Have we remembered everything and everyone? What is important to you and to your loved one?

Carol shares how she was determined to make her mother's last days ones that she and her family would remember with love forever.

Carol

Mom took us all by surprise when she decided to 'do MAID' while the family was visiting rather than wait until after they left like she'd planned. One moment, she had some vague idea that it would be after the kids left and the next moment, in her determined way, Mom told me to call up the MAID people and set the date right away because it would be 'easier for Carol' if she died while I had the support of my whole family.

I'll never forget the look on Mom's face when I told her the date and time of her MAID death. Her face was suffused with light and joy. She actually clapped her hands together and exclaimed, "That's wonderful!"

During what was to be her last week, I was determined to do everything humanly possible to make each of her days perfect. I was like a whirlwind, meeting with the minister, taking her

137

library books back, setting up visits with friends (she only wanted to see a very few), making a dinner reservation for the family for 'after,' taking her for drives, and making sure everyone in the family was okay.

My mother was one of the most determined people I know. When she made a decision, she followed through. I inherited that trait from her, for which I am very grateful, because determination helped me survive the last days with a smile on my face and love in my heart.

On the day before MAID, I took Mom and my best friend, who had been a part of my life since I was five years old, for a long, leisurely drive around West Vancouver. We exclaimed at the big houses and the beautiful views, chatted about when we were kids, and had a magical time. And then in the evening, I went to visit Mom by myself. I sat on her bed and told her she was an amazing mother. We are not a very demonstrative family, and I realized that I hadn't told her often enough how much I loved her. I was determined to make up for it that night. She smiled and thanked me and then said she needed to sleep.

I drove home, but even when alone in the car, I would not allow myself to cry. There would be time for tears later. I was determined to stay focused only on making sure that the next day—Mom's last—would be a good one.

How Do You Feel?
How did you say goodbye to your loved one? Did you have goals or a list of things to achieve? How did it feel for you?

138

DISBELIEF

Few things in life are more bizarre than living through the days and hours leading up to the planned death of a loved one. How can we register that there are two hours left, one hour left, thirty minutes left? Because doing so is so difficult, even impossible, many people suspend their knowledge of reality. They focus on the present rather than on the immediate future.

Brittney shares how she felt disbelief mingled with joy while witnessing the last hours of her mother's life.

Brittney

The drive to the hospital was a blur. My boyfriend drove, my sister sat in the back seat, and I don't think anyone spoke for the entire thirty-minute journey. We were going to the hospital to be with my mom for her final few hours, to say goodbye and then to ultimately watch her pass away. The day before, she had decided that she was ready.

I felt like I was in the twilight zone, just total disbelief, as I walked into the hospice room where my mom was sitting up in bed. My stepdad stood by her side, along with my sister and our two aunts, one of whom was my mother's identical twin.

Texts sent to my mom were being read out loud. "I love you" and "Thanks for being such a great aunt." It was both heartbreaking and heart-warming hearing these messages, and I can only imagine how hard, and just plain surreal it must have been for my cousins to send these goodbye texts.

The procedure was scheduled for 12:30 pm. I kept looking at the clock. At just 32, I was being forced to say goodbye to my mom. I felt numb, as though I was in the twilight zone, in a bad dream. I thought, *This can't be my life right now.*

139

Chapter 5

The doctor came in at 11:30 and asked, "Are you sure this is what you want?" My mom nodded her head and gave a thumbs up. My heart sank. I could not believe my mom was about to leave us. At noon, a nurse came in to let us know that the doctor would return in 30 minutes. It wasn't a dream; this was real life.

The hours leading up to my moms' passing were exactly how she wanted. We listened to music. It started with sad songs that I still have a hard time listening to, such as Celine Dion's, *My Heart Will Go On* and *Sound of Silence* by Disturbed. Then Creedence Clearwater Revival's *Up Around the Bend* came on and we got up and started dancing. We stood in a circle, held hands, and literally danced and did the jig. It was hilarious. We laughed and danced through the entire song. My mom had the best moves, and we had no idea where she got this energy from! She was ready to go. Her mood that morning was almost cheerful and excited. She was ready to be pain free. No more pain pump, no more feeding tube, no more cancer.

My mom loved music. Her last message on her marker board read, "I love you all, thank you for helping me be pain free," followed by, "Can we have a nice song on?" I hugged her and told her I loved her. Witnessing my family say their goodbyes was so surreal, and just plain bizarre. My body and brain felt like jello. I couldn't even think properly. I like to think of the beginning lyrics of *Up Around the Bend*: "There's a place up ahead and I'm going, just as fast as my feet can fly, come away, come away if you're going, leave this sinking ship behind."

How Do You Feel?
What were the most and least comforting moments of your loved one's goodbye'?

LONELY

The days leading up to the planned death of your loved one can feel incredibly lonely, even if family and friends surround you. How can you cope knowing that very soon you will truly be alone? It's hard to imagine that anyone can be feeling the same way you are, or that anyone will understand the magnitude of the loss you are about to experience.

Cathy shares how she felt as she and her husband shared their last days together, and Geneviève shares how she stayed strong by *not* saying goodbye.

Cathy

Gary and I said our goodbyes at the beginning of his illness, rather than at the end. It wasn't really the beginning because the seeds of his disease had been planted 50 years ago when he couldn't pass up a lucrative summer job insulating industrial smokestacks that were filled with asbestos.

We at first hoped he 'just' had pneumonia, but the final diagnosis was mesothelioma and the respirologist told us there was no hope, no cure. How did we deal with such terrible news? After the initial shock, we talked and talked and talked. We held each other in bed each night and remembered our life together and how good it had been. He turned to me one night just as I was drifting off and asked with awe and wonder "what if I'd never met you?" which might have been the sweetest thing anyone has ever said to me. So, it was then, night after night, that we essentially said our goodbyes.

Over the next year and a half, our lives normalized for a while, and then quickly deteriorated. I keep a daily journal and one day I talked about buying enough apple butter to last us for a year. But then I caught myself and wrote: *But having said that, I'm not sure that Gary will last that long. He's weak, walking very slowly and struggling to get out of the car, and he sleeps most of the day. It feels like I'm losing him piece by piece. We used to talk all the time as we both went about our relatively busy lives. We still talk, but it's just about the essentials ... no more light-hearted banter and I miss that. In fact, I miss him and he's still here.*

It was early November when Gary looked at me and said, "It's time." I contacted the MAID team, and the process was scheduled for three days later. Friends and family filed in during those three days to say their goodbyes. Gary was in pain and exhausted and there was little time for us to talk. We both withdrew into ourselves as we struggled to get our heads around what was happening. On the one hand, I felt relief. He would no longer be sick and in pain, and I could stop monitoring him every minute to see how he was doing. But on the other, his death was unthinkable.

We had always been so close. We could say anything and everything to each other. But he was moving beyond me, and I found myself wondering if there is anything lonelier than missing the person you love when they're sitting across from you. I yearned for the early days after the diagnosis, when the love we felt for each other was magnified by the knowledge that it would end.

Now, our energy was directed to dealing with his pain and getting through the days. It was no way for the sweetest relationship of my life to end.

Geneviève

Leading up to our MAID date, my husband and I had an enormous number of conversations about death, but these were more about his decision to die rather than how we wanted to say goodbye. It was hard to acknowledge what was actually happening, even though everything we were doing was to help him die.

I felt very alone, and knew I was going to be alone going forward, so rightly or wrongly, I decided I needed to stay strong. In order to do that, I could not say an actual 'goodbye'.'

Instead, we planned time together. We took small trips to our cabin or on the road, organized date nights and picnics, and went for lovely walks, hand in hand. We did not cut ourselves off completely from others, but neither did we reach out very often. It was a time where I felt incredibly alone and isolated even though my husband and I were together almost continuously. It was the worst kind of alone, being with someone who wanted to die and who was unhappy and not himself.

We also spent time with our children, especially at the cabin, going for family bike rides, roasting marshmallows on the fire at night, and playing games. I was trying to make moments happen, to be supportive and to protect myself from feeling too much. Our goodbyes were more about the moments than the actual words. I wanted our time together to be pleasurable and memorable, not just sad.

How Do You Feel?

Did you feel lonely in the days before your loved one died? Write about your feelings of loneliness.

GUILTY

With so much going on during the last days before your loved one's death, it's natural that guilt should play a role. Guilt can take many forms — from having feelings that you don't think are 'right,' to feeling like you're not helping your loved one enough, to not knowing how to talk to others while still respecting your loved one's privacy. How do you navigate these uncharted

Chapter 5

waters? Guilt is a draining emotion, but in some ways, it's easier to feel guilty about what we are doing in any given moment than to face the full weight of grief that's about to take over.

Shannon, Elizabeth, and Robin each share how feelings of guilt challenged them during their loved one's last days.

Shannon

We spent a lot of time watching *Ted Lasso* in the two weeks leading up to Wendy's MAID date. It was heart-warming and funny and kept the mood light at times.

One morning, I arrived at Wendy's place at four in the morning to watch the Canadian Women's National Hockey team play overseas. I was welcomed into the quiet home with an '*Oiiiiiii!!!*' from Wendy and her sister. (If you've seen *Ted Lasso*, you'll know Roy — thank you Jason Sudeikis) I was extremely grateful for this time. The mornings were quiet, and Wendy had more energy to chat and laugh.

I also found myself feeling conflicted. Our own local hockey team did not know that Wendy was moving forward with MAID in only a few days. I don't know why she allowed me to be present and not others. I struggled deeply with not being able to tell our teammates, our friends. They were my support people. It was a choice between respecting Wendy's wishes and reaching out for the support I needed. It was a choice between Wendy's privacy and my own well-being.

I felt suspended in guilt for fourteen days. I felt guilty for keeping her secret and guilty for letting it slip to one friend. It was difficult to navigate. I was wrung out with anxiety and despair. I had sobbing fits, writhing in agony on the floor, alone in my home, not being able to catch my breath, caught in a fierce, silent exhale with my heart pounding between my ears. My dog would hover over me, concerned, doing her best to comfort me.

Saying Goodbye

This is so unfair. Unfair that Wendy is sick. Unfair she's dying. Unfair beyond words, all of it.

With the days dwindling, I wrote Wendy a letter. It was short, direct, and to the point. It wasn't a goodbye, more of a 'thank you, you've impacted me.' I said exactly what I needed to say, nothing more and nothing less. As unfair as all of this was, I at least had that opportunity to say goodbye; and now she had given me the opportunity to truly live and feel the human experience.

Elizabeth

My mom was a very private person and requested that the witnesses, Dad, myself and my siblings, be the only people who were aware of her decision to have a medically assisted death. MAID was a very new end-of-life choice in 2016, so few people were aware of it. I suspect she did not want to be judged for her choice or be obliged to explain it to multitudes of people.

This was extremely difficult to deal with because there were a few people in the extended family and some dear friends who would be completely heartbroken if they could not say goodbye to her. I felt so dishonest about trying to have normal conversations with some of these people, knowing what was about to happen and not saying anything. I felt like a fake.

I decided with my siblings to reach out to a very few people that fell into this category so that they could either visit or call and speak with Mom. I was feeling an incredible amount of guilt that I wasn't completely respecting her wishes. We had a very honest relationship, but this pushed things to a different level. I felt like a failure and a traitor to her. What good was I as a daughter if I couldn't respect some of her final wishes?

However, I was able to give these family and friends a proper opportunity to say goodbye, and I think it was very comforting to

Chapter 5

Mom. In fact, she ended up telling the people that visited and called about her choice for medically assisted death.

It was very similar with my father in 2021, except that the same circle of family and friends were pretty aware of what he wanted, so although shocking, it wasn't unexpected.

Robin

When you're a single parent with a full-time job, having an ill parent is a perfect path to being consumed by guilt. That's probably the case in any situation.

My dad was living in a seniors' lodge — not the cheeriest of places. He'd gone from a house where he gardened and talked to his neighbours to living in a single room and eating cafeteria food, with, as he put it, a bunch of cranky old people.

I did what I could, bringing him snacks and his favourite chocolate bars, and taking him out for lunch or a milkshake when he felt up to it. When he texted and asked me to bring a bottle of laundry detergent or some more cough drops, I was relieved because it was something I could do to help, and it got me out of the endless mental loop of wondering if I should be doing more.

About a month before he died, my dad moved to a long-term care home. The room was better, if very like a hospital, and the whole environment was brighter. It didn't do much for my guilt, however, which sat high in my chest and fluttered like a butterfly. It was always there, an accompaniment to the guilty thoughts that rolled around my brain. *I should be doing more to help him.* (Flutter.) *I need to visit him more.* (Flutter, flutter.) *I'm a terrible daughter.* (Flutter, flutter, FLUTTER.)

When he told us he was going ahead with MAID the following week, the guilt kicked into overdrive. I wondered if it was because he was depressed and lonely. That wasn't why — his health had continued to decline very quickly, and he no longer had good

146

quality of life, but the guilt butterfly flapped its wings and suggested it anyway.

With the date looming, we moved into planning his final days. I took my kids to see him and say goodbye. My sister and I picked him up and took him for a drive past my parents' old house and across the new bridge in town that had recently been completed and that he wanted to see. He visited his best friend a final time, and we went to my sister's and brother's houses so he could say one last goodbye to his grandkids.

When I think about those last days, I think about knowing the date my dad would die and counting down day by day, and the guilt I still feel about whether I should have done more for him in his last months of life. The guilt butterfly remains with me, and I wonder if it always will.

How Do You Feel?

Did you experience guilt during the days before your loved one's medically assisted death? What did you feel guilty about? Consider how guilt influenced how you acted and interacted with others.

EXHAUSTED

Exhaustion can play a major role in the MAID journey. When a loved one's illness extends for months or years, particularly if you are the caregiver, exhaustion may become a daily challenge. Or perhaps you just feel exhausted from the rollercoaster ride of constantly changing emotions.

Jane shares how exhausted she felt by the time her husband chose his MAID day.

Chapter 5

Jane

By the time my husband was ready to make the call to the MAID provider to set a date to die, I was exhausted. It had been two years since he was accepted for MAID. It had been a tough journey for both of us and we were worn out. It was hard to watch him deteriorate and suffer and not be able to take that away. It felt like I had lead boots on as I went about trying to ensure he had the proper care each day.

When he was finally ready to make the call, I made myself be cheery, inviting family over for casual visits. Everyone knew why they were invited, but my husband didn't want to talk about *it*. I think I was punch drunk trying to get my mind and body to do and say all the right things.

In the end, I couldn't cope with the game anymore, and my husband agreed to be open with his visitors. I didn't sleep much even though I needed to; my mind kept going over what was happening. It seemed surreal that my husband would be dead on Friday morning.

There were two days of visiting family, and I was glad of the distraction. I could do little else but sit and watch, feeling like all the air was being sucked out of me.

How Do You Feel?

What did you find most exhausting about saying goodbye to your loved one?

SCARED

How will we survive without our loved one? That is a commonly expressed fear, and no wonder! You've loved your person, possibly for decades, and now you are supposed to manage without them? How is that possible? Facing life without them in it, is one of the scariest things to think about.

Bobbie shares the fear she felt contemplating a life without her beloved husband Bob.

Bobbie

After 23 years as his caregiver, my husband wanted me to enjoy my life to the fullest. I would cry and say "How can I do anything without you? We are always together, and you are my biggest cheerleader." He told me he had given me the wings to fly and that he believed I could do it.

He wanted me to read for hours, ride my bike, play tennis, and go back to my arts—all the things I had cut back on or stopped doing to be his caregiver. I felt so empty because I had only enjoyed those pursuits because he was encouraging me. I didn't care if I did any of those things again. We had been married over 51 years and we were known as a pair. Bob and Bobbie. Not one without the other. The fear of tomorrow was so overwhelming that I don't think I understood what was about to happen. *How could there be a tomorrow for me, and not for Bob? I didn't want it if he was not going to be in it!*

I allowed myself to cry in Bob's arms at night when we went to bed, remembering our fabulous life together and talking about our memories. I was doing my best to be supportive, presenting well to the outside world while I was terrified inside.

How Do You Feel?
What makes you feel the most scared about your loved one's medically assisted death? Is it related to MAID or life without them?

Chapter 5

DISAPPOINTED

Your expectation of what it will be like to say goodbye to your loved one may not match the reality. They may be too weak or too scared to participate, or just unable to say and do the things we hoped for. When this happens, you may feel disappointed, even angry. Why can't everything go the way you want? But of course, that's life, and death. It's not necessarily romantic, or the way we imagine it in our mind. Sometimes, we must find ways to gather our strength even in the midst of disappointment.

Nikki shares how she coped during the last difficult days before her dad passed.

Nikki

I wished people would stop telling me how lucky I was to have that time with my dad. It really was a special kind of hell we were living in. Saying goodbye was not what I thought it would be. Our evenings together were not spent with my dad thanking me for being an incredible caretaker/daughter/advocate/punching bag.

Instead, I ran around like a chicken with its head cut off, trying to make sure that everyone else was taken care of. Were the kids home from school/fed/put to bed so that I could get back to my dad's and lie beside him in bed while he told me about how shit my family was? He basically unloaded all his anger and disappointment on me. I would lie there quietly—half drunk and half stoned, holding space and choking back my tears. Choking back my desire to argue in defence of everyone he was complaining about.

I couldn't actually believe this was how it was all ending. "Ok, Dad. I hear you. I understand. That's an awful way to feel. I'm so sorry this is what you've been thinking and carrying for all these years. That must be really hard." *I just want to go home and have a shower. Maybe I could wash off some of his negative energy.* I wanted to hold my babies close and cuddle my husband. I wanted to weep quietly in the shower, so nobody would hear or know the depth of my pain and anguish.

It was two nights prior to his MAID provision before he would finally discuss funeral plans with me. He did not want one, which was fine with me because the last thing I wanted to do was organize a gathering and see people and have to answer questions. I didn't particularly want to see my own family any more than I needed to, either. Again, I felt so isolated, back on that raft in the middle of the ocean with no land in sight.

I told him I couldn't bear the idea of burying him. He agreed to cremation. It's cheaper anyway. I loved that—frugal all the way until the end. With that decided, I gathered myself and crawled out of his bed. I felt like mercury forming back together into human form each time I pulled myself back together. I tucked him in, kissed his head, and shut off the lights.

The next night was no better. In fact, it was worse. My brother came. *Nice of you to join us. Welcome to hell.*

The nurse arrived to put in his IV lines. She was an angel. My dad flirted with her and was actually quite funny. I cherished this, that even 12 hours before his death, he managed to be charming and make me laugh, true to form, even while staring death in the face. Unfortunately, that was short-lived. We called my brother's children on FaceTime so he could say goodbye one last time. I tried to lighten the mood by saying that it's just a see-you-later and we will all meet again on the other side.

"Shut up, you fucking asshole!" my dad yelled at me. I could hear my heartbreak ringing through my hot ears. *Wow. Ok.* I pretended that didn't happen. The grandkids said goodbye, and I led my dad to bed. I lay with him a while and thanked him for all the things he taught me, for being the dad he was, which made me the strong woman I am today. I framed everything in a way that was kind. His lessons to me were hard, and he was tough, and so I had to be, to survive him.

But I did. And I am strong, and I am grateful even though the wounds are deep.

How Do You Feel?
Were you disappointed with how you said goodbye? What would you want to be different? Write about how your expectations of saying goodbye may or may not have matched what actually happened.

CONFLICTED

Many storytellers used the word 'surreal' to describe the experience of saying goodbye to their loved one. They felt like they were living in a kind of alternate universe where nothing was as it should be, and conflicting emotions bounced off each other.

Carole shares how she felt conflicted during the lead-up to the passing of her friend.

Carole

I wasn't ready.

I'm not sure how anyone can really prepare themselves to say goodbye forever. In such a surreal situation, the finality of it was the most perplexing. On the one hand, I was definitely supportive of Dan's courage to exit peacefully and on his own terms, but my heart was distraught at the thought of not being able to interact with him ever again. It was these conflicting and confusing emotions that were having a wrestling match inside my head.

Saying Goodbye

To diffuse the situation mentally, I had to find something to do. Sue (Dan's wife) was sitting very close to him, squeezing his hand tightly and whispering private words lovingly to him. I had to applaud her courage as I kneeled by Dan's feet and asked if he'd like a relaxing foot massage. This made him giggle, but yes, he would like to try one. Being the Dan I knew and loved, it was inevitable for him to make a joke that this would be his first and last one. After a few minutes of comfort, he asked that I continue throughout the procedure because he found it very soothing. Dan also seemed soothed to hear a few comical memories we shared, but in between the laughter (and maybe even during), I struggled emotionally to make peace with these complicated, confusing thoughts that wouldn't be silenced.

I still haven't resolved these conflicting emotions. That being said, I wholeheartedly (in hindsight) still support his decision to have a MAID procedure; but for me, it still hurts so much not to have him around.

Losing a dear friend in any circumstances is hard so I'm not sure if this compounded it for me, but as days pass and warm, loving memories of our interactions in life float intermittently through my psyche, I'm gradually beginning to be more resolved and certainly prouder of Dan for his choice.

MAID eased his pain, and time will ease mine.

How Do You Feel?
Did you feel conflicting emotions while saying goodbye to your loved one? Can you identify them?

Chapter 5

SADNESS

Losing a loved one hurts, and the pain never really goes away. A challenge when saying goodbye is balancing the pain and sadness you feel with the desire to put on a brave face and make things less difficult for your loved one.

Emily shares how she coped with the sadness of losing the two most important people in the world to her in less than a year.

Emily

My story comes with a twist when it comes to saying goodbye. You see, my mother and my spouse, Veronica, were both battling terminal cancer at the same time. My mother died two hundred and fourteen days before the day Veronica decided to die.

Saying goodbye was something that I was able to do with my mother, but man, did it hurt. I felt so broken inside when my mother died, and I knew I would have to go through it again when Veronica died. My thoughts and feeling were so jumbled up that I didn't know what was what. All I knew was that my two best friends in this whole entire world were going to die from cancer and there was nothing I could do to stop it.

I felt so helpless, broken, and hurt, but I didn't dare show it to them when they were here because I didn't want them to worry about me. I played it off that I was going to be okay and that I'd go right back to work, and everything would be fine. That wasn't the case. My heart broke into a million pieces and there was no way to describe the feelings.

My tears flowed when Veronica was not around. I didn't want to make it harder for her. This process was unique, to say the least. Getting the opportunity to say my goodbye was a gift that I will never ever forget. The love that we got to express to each other, and hearing Veronica say thank you for everything that I did for her, was priceless. Veronica never, ever liked the word goodbye. She asked me to say "see you later" instead.

So, our goodbye was a 'see you later.' I didn't know what she was going through when she walked away from me in the bedroom. I never stopped her. I knew I had to let her process this day the way she needed to for herself. I couldn't imagine what she was thinking or if she was scared. I don't know because she never told me, and I didn't ask her. I didn't want to stir up unnecessary thoughts or feelings. Veronica put on a very brave face for me, and I hid my pain and devastation from her.

How Do You Feel?

How did you cope with the pain and sadness of saying goodbye? Were you able to express your feelings, or did you hold them in? How did that affect you?

RESIGNED

Contemplating a future without your loved one can leave you feeling like you're about to walk into a desert, devoid of comfort and with nowhere to get your bearings, nowhere to be comfortable ever again. Your entire world is being turned upside down. You know what is coming and you can't stop it. You may even be prepared for it, but it doesn't feel any better. You have no choice but to proceed.

Cynthia shares how, even though she felt prepared for the death of her husband, she wasn't prepared for how unremarkable it would be to say goodbye.

Chapter 5

Cynthia

It's strange and unnerving to know the date that someone is going to die. I couldn't help but feel like it was my job to create a series of perfect moments and fulfil a bucket list of activities with smiles and loving embraces.

But how? This felt so unrealistic, so contrived. We had two young, active kids grieving with us. Everyone was tired and overwhelmed with the weight of his death day looming. I was anxious and finding it hard to sleep. My mind constantly wandered to thoughts of the end, of after, of the funeral, of life as a widow and the mother of two fatherless kids, of my capacity to support their grief on top of my own.

My husband was sleeping 12 to 16 hours a day, and some days his legs didn't work. He was ready to die. During this time, I wanted to be fun mom, or patient mom or silly mom, but all I seemed to succeed at was bitchy, angry, tired, and sad mom. It felt like I was failing and I couldn't imagine where I was going to get the energy to help my kids through their dad's death.

My husband was determined to reserve the best time, the most time, for his kids — to tuck them in every night, to cuddle them, and to infuse them with his love and his memory. He relied on me to be his gatekeeper, his time watcher, his bad guy, so he could love his kids for every possible second before he left us.

The night before he died, the four of us stayed up late finishing the book we had been reading as a family. We ordered take-out from one of our regular restaurants and had a cozy dinner in bed. By this point, our master bedroom had become like a second living room.

When I finally made it to bed, he was already sleeping. As I cuddled up to him, I noticed how unremarkable this moment felt. This was my last night as my husband's wife. *Wasn't it supposed to feel more memorable? More special? More...desperate, like the goodbye before his brain surgery had felt the previous year?*

I thought back to that difficult goodbye ten months earlier. My husband's tears had started to flow hearing his children say goodbye as we left for the hospital. When the nurse came to take him into his surgery, his tears flowed again as he transferred his thick platinum wedding band onto my thumb for safekeeping. When I pulled him close, he clung to me. He did not want to die in surgery! It was the most cherished hug of my life.

The night before my husband's death, I lay next to his sick, weak body and realized that this *should* feel unremarkable. I didn't feel from him the desperate fear, the desire to stay, or the clinging of a man with goals and unfinished business that I'd felt ten months earlier. He was sick, tired, anxious, resigned...and ready to die.

I summoned the feeling of that cherished hug from ten months earlier, then wrapped my arms tightly around myself and sobbed.

How Do You Feel?

Did you feel resigned? Describe what resignation felt like for you.

WHAT'S YOUR STORY?

Saying goodbye to someone forever is both an opportunity and a challenge. It can feel like an enormous responsibility to make the most of the moment and not get it wrong, while also trying to say goodbye in a way that is authentic and realistic, given the circumstances and health of your loved one.

Listed below are each of the emotions presented as our storytellers said goodbye to their loved one.

- Grateful
- Acceptance
- Relieved
- Determined
- Disbelief
- Lonely
- Guilty

- Exhausted
- Scared
- Disappointed
- Conflicted
- Hurt
- Resigned

How Do You Feel?

Which emotions and stories resonate with you?

Which emotions do not resonate with you?

What emotions did you feel as you said goodbye to your loved one that were not included?

Did anything you felt while saying goodbye surprise you?

CHAPTER 6 -

MAID DAY

Let us not look back in anger, nor forward in fear, but around in awareness. — James Thurber

MAID day has finally arrived. For some of us, the journey was long and arduous; for others, it came quickly or even with ease. But regardless of how long we waited, planned, and prepared for our loved one's MAID day, none of us were truly ready.

How can we make sense of something so beyond our normal experience? We know people will die, but we usually don't know when they will die. With MAID, we had an appointment with health care providers who arrived to fulfill our loved one's request to help them die. Many of us championed our loved one's choice to have MAID, but that didn't mean we wanted them to die, or were ready to lose them forever.

Our storytellers share the pain and the relief, the anxiety and the love they experienced during the last hours and minutes they spent with their loved one on MAID day.

Chapter 6

NUMB

Sometimes the only way to survive a difficult time is to numb our emotions, to effectively put them on hold and then take them out and experience them on another day when they might not be quite so painful. MAID day may only be survivable when we turn off our emotions so we can be fully present for our loved one.

Dave B. and Geneviève share their sense of numbness and absence of feelings on their loved one's MAID day.

Dave B.

Annie's death came within twelve hours of her decision that she was ready to die. After two nights of sleeplessness and pain, she decided one morning, her last morning, that this was the day she would have MAID. "Going to die tonight," she wrote in a note to me.

We had lived for over a year knowing that Annie's death was imminent, but without a firm 'day of,' it always felt like her death was off in the future. It might have been inevitable and not far off, but it still wasn't in the immediate present. We were both mostly concerned about day-to-day living — me with doing my best to care for her, and her just coping with the challenges of eating and drinking and communicating.

And then, all of a sudden, one day it was the 'day of.'

"Going to die tonight."

I read her familiar handwriting on the note she passed me.

Numbness and shock overwhelmed me. There was nothing left for me to do now. There were no more errands to run, no more talking to doctors or home care nurses on her behalf. I felt like my role, my purpose, had popped like a soap bubble. I felt a mad scramble of 'what-nowism?' She was such a huge part of who I was — I was in the world in the way that she saw me. Now there would be no Annie to see me anymore.

Annie's adult children and I said our goodbyes as she lay on the living room sofa with the IV in her arm, ready and eager for the drugs to be administered. She couldn't speak but had her notepad and Sharpie with her.

"Goodbye, I love you all," was her final note. To call it heart-wrenching seems inadequate. Instead, I felt more numbness and shock.

I felt like I was watching a movie through a screen, purely a spectator, as her gentle doctor administered the drugs. It was as though we were detached observers; we watched her pulse throb in her neck and then stop. We hugged each other when it was over, and our eyes were wet, but for me anyway, everything we'd just witnessed felt remote.

She died gently, and the prospect of spending the rest of my life without her at the centre of it, started to break into my consciousness.

Geneviève

The day of my husband's death took forever to arrive and then came all at once. The night before, his sister and brother came into town to be with us. We had a great dinner and danced and sang until late. It was a really fun evening, which was a bit odd, considering the circumstances.

We woke early, ate breakfast, dressed nicely — my husband wore a suit, shirt and tie — and headed to the hospital for 9 AM. I was on autopilot as I ate and drove us to his appointment. My husband had decided to donate his organs, which meant he needed to die in a hospital so he could immediately be taken to a surgical room after he was pronounced dead.

Chapter 6

We checked in and went up to the floor where MAID would occur, and I realized that I hadn't registered anything that had happened. I was totally numb. We went for a walk while we waited for everything to be in order. I remember that I held my husband's hand tightly. I didn't want to let go.

It wasn't long before we were back in the room, my husband undressing and changing into a hospital gown. The doctors spoke with him privately—a final check in to see if he had any reservations or if he had changed his mind.

And then it was time.

I pulled a chair up beside the bed. I held his hand and with my other I held my childrens' hands. There were three or four injections, I cannot really remember. When they gave him the first one, I told him that I loved him and I thanked him for our wonderful life. After the second injection, he asked the nurse how she had gotten into this line of nursing, which made me laugh. He fell asleep before she was able to answer and then he started to snore. I expected it to be over rather quickly, but my husband was in very good shape and his heart kept beating for 45 minutes after he had stopped breathing[2].

When we were finally told he was gone, I let go of his hand. I realized that I had cried throughout most of the procedure, but silently, without noticing. I got up and hugged the nurse who provided MAID, and before I knew it, we were in the elevator and going to the street. I can't really remember driving home. Even after I'd been home for hours, the numbness had still not left my body. I think I ate lunch and then I went for a lie-down, but I ended up crying instead. Slowly, my sadness started coming out.

---

[2] Generally, a person who is administered the drugs used for a medically assisted death will die within a few minutes.

How Do You Feel?

Did you feel numb on the day your loved one had MAID? What is the first emotion you can recall when the numbness subsided?

RESIGNED

When our loved one chooses MAID, particularly if they've expressed their wish for a long time, we may find ourselves feeling resigned on the day. So many emotions have passed through us in the weeks and months prior that there's nothing left but resignation.

Carole shares how she struggled to put aside her own grief and resign herself to focusing only on helping Dan's wife Sue cope with his passing.

Carole

When Sue called to tell me that Dan's passing was imminent, I wasn't exactly taken aback because I was fully aware of the delicate state of his current health. I received this latest update with overwhelming grief but tried hard to just be resigned and solid for Sue's sake.

But when she informed me of the exact date of his 'passing,' I frantically tried to analyze the implication of what she sounded hesitant to convey. Dan had made a personal choice to avail himself of the MAID process, and Sue was doing her absolute best to support his decision. Struggling with her own strong religious beliefs was challenging for her, but with her usual determination and her love for her husband of over 40 years, she was trying to respect and support him, no matter what. Now I had the task of resigning myself to sympathize with Sue's discomfort and still support Dan's bravery.

I hoped that when I was actually present with them 'on the day,' I would be able to rely on natural empathetic instincts to somehow channel the most appropriate way to talk with them. Fortunately, this proved to be the case. I listened as the MAID lady, with utmost compassion, clearly and gently addressed all their concerns. I witnessed a truly skilled professional bring about a calm, peaceful acceptance of what to expect. Her affable, approachable manner was perfectly in tune with Sue's concerns and certainly eased her anxiety.

For the next while, I tried to allow myself to be present and to be a comfort to both Dan and Sue, and to be resigned as much as I could that this was Dan's personal journey.

That special place that Dan held in my heart will never be occupied. I'll never forget Dan, but I was resigned to his departure.

How Do You Feel?

Can you recall feeling resigned during your loved one's MAID journey?

NERVOUS

The body has its own agenda when it comes to coping with difficult situations. While our logical mind may be supportive, resigned, and even calm, our bodies physically manifest the emotions we can't or don't want to acknowledge or express.

Robin shares how nerves took a toll on her on the day her father had MAID.

MAID Day

Robin

On the day of my dad's MAID provision, I woke up early and threw up. We knew he had been considering MAID, but when it came time, we only had a week's notice. My nervousness and anxiety grew over the week until on that day I couldn't contain it anymore.

The day felt incredibly long as we waited until 2 pm when the doctor was booked to come. I dreaded going to the long-term care facility that my dad was in because I knew it would be for the last time and I would leave those doors having lost him.

I'm a habitual breakfast eater, but I couldn't eat that morning. My stomach was filled with butterflies, and I had a massive headache. I choked down a Tylenol and some water, but I knew I was going to need to force myself to eat something. I stopped at the Tim Horton's across the street from Dad's care home, but hadn't considered there would be a line. I couldn't spend any of my dad's last hours in a line-up waiting for a muffin, so I went to the gas station next door where I ended up with a Coke and a hot dog—a gas station hot dog, which under normal circumstances I wouldn't even consider eating.

It did the trick, though, and I was able to calm myself enough to join my siblings and be with my dad. I managed to talk and joke with him and listen to his classic stories, at least until the nurse came, at which point the stomach butterflies launched into flight again. His provision was scheduled for 2:00 but the nurse came at 1:30 to insert an IV, and I wasn't ready.

My breath was shallow, and my chest tightened. I swallowed, trying to get the lump in my throat to prevent the tears from falling, but I wasn't successful. All the effort I had made to keep my emotions in check gave way like a dam being washed down a flooding river. I had to let it all flow. The time had come to say goodbye to my dad.

Chapter 6

APPREHENSIVE

Most of us have no reference points for how we think we should act on the day our loved one has chosen to die. How can we be prepared? What will we feel? Will we be able to show up for our loved one to support them? What's going to happen?

All these questions can lead to feelings of apprehension and anxiety. Three of our storytellers share how they coped with these emotions on MAID day.

Jane

We had an early morning appointment, so we were both up very early on the day of George's medically assisted death. My stomach was in knots. In my mind, there was a lot to do. In reality, it was my apprehension and nerves that looked for things to do so I could keep myself busy.

Since my husband didn't like needles, I was given some numbing cream to put on the needle site in advance. That's when the 'what ifs' started. *What if the needle still hurt? What if someone not invited showed up? What if the provider was late? What if it didn't work? What if I couldn't be brave? What if I didn't want to see him die?*

And the biggest what if of all — *what if he changed his mind?*

My breathing quickened, and I felt jittery inside. I had to keep moving, but I wanted to be with my husband as well. He was looking to me for reassurance, and I wasn't sure I could give it to him.

MAID Day

The nurse had trouble with the IV site and in the end, the procedure did hurt. George turned to me in pain, and I tried to comfort him. It took all my strength to appear unfazed. Voices in my head shouted at me, demanding that I stay calm. My shoulders and neck tightened, and I could feel my jaw clench. It felt like we were in a surreal universe.

The doctor came, which provided me with an outlet for some of my pent-up energy as I got her settled. We sat beside my husband while she calmly reviewed their previous conversations, explained the procedure, and asked George if he wanted to continue. I noticed a calm begin to spread through my body as she spoke. I felt myself letting go of the apprehension. This WAS real, and it would be over soon.

When the procedure started, the room became very quiet. George looked at me one last time and then he was gone. I felt a tremendous amount of peace and even allowed myself a little smile. It was over. A huge weight had been lifted off my heart. He was at peace and so was I.

Elizabeth

My nerves were shot. I felt like throwing up and I was terrified that I would pass out.

Those emotions and feelings happened to me on both my parents' MAID days. My mother had MAID first and then, several years later, my father was fortunate to have the same MAID provider for his death.

Don't for one minute think that I wasn't grieving and sad. I think that goes without saying when you lose someone you love, but there were so many other feelings that came along with this kind of a death.

Both of my parents chose to die at home. I nervously awaited the doctor as the time neared. A sense of dread came over me,

Chapter 6

knowing this was really the end. My heart was racing and inside I was screaming.

No! It's too soon!

The doctor arrived and obtained final consent from the 'patient' to go ahead with the procedure. An IV was started, and the drugs were delivered in a well-choreographed dance.

I wanted to look away and scream, but both times, I held their hands as they slipped away. It really happened so fast, maybe five minutes or less. It was incredibly peaceful for both of them, and for that I was grateful. They had both suffered so much pain in their last years of life. I was relieved, honoured, and at peace.

Brittney

We were gathered around my mom's bed in the hospital's hospice room. I could hear staff conversing in the hallway and faint beeping noises from the neighbouring rooms. I sat at the end of the bed with my hands around my mom's toes, which were covered with a cozy blanket. The doctor was kind and gentle as he quietly went over what was about to happen.

"There are three IV's, the first one ...." I honestly don't remember what he said. I didn't really want to know. The doctor looked over at my mom and for the last time, he asked her if she was ready, if this was still what she wanted? She smiled, nodded and gave him the thumbs up.

I was scared as hell.

Will this hurt her?

Is she as upset and scared as we are?

OMG, I am not ready.

I'm not ready to not have a mother anymore!

Dammit, I hate cancer!

MAID Day

The doctor held my mom's hand as he administered the first medication into her IV. They smiled at each other, and she mouthed the words "thank you" to him.

I felt numb. Nothing else mattered in the world. I didn't give a shit about the normal things people worry about, like work and bills. I just wanted my mom. We held her and surrounded her with love, calmness and warmth as she fell asleep for the very last time. It only took a few seconds. Just like that, she was gone. It was peaceful, which was exactly what she wanted.

The room went quiet. I could no longer hear staff talking or the beeping from next door. It was like the world had stopped turning and everything stood still. Silence, peace, calmness. Nothing-ness. The doctor, me, and everyone else in the room had tears running down our faces. He checked her pulse and then quietly left the room. My strong feeling of anxiety still lingered.

Now what? I thought, as I looked at her lifeless, but very peaceful body. *What do we do now?*

I hadn't thought this far ahead. I slowly picked up my purse, my sweater and the iced cappuccino that I had barely touched. The last thing I wanted to do was eat. I felt so nauseous and empty inside, as if someone had ripped my heart out of my body. I noticed my mom's purse, which seemed so out-of-place now that she was gone. A pair of glasses she had purchased from my work sat on top. *What do we do with her purse?*

I took the glasses and a tube of lip balm and moved them into my purse, and then I sat myself down on a chair next to my mom's body and cried. *I don't have a mom anymore.* My head was down, with my hands covering my face. The anxiety got to me; I couldn't be strong anymore.

I had entered the hospital just a few hours ago with a mother, and now I was leaving as a heartbroken, anxious, motherless child.

Chapter 6

How Do You Feel?
Did apprehension and anxiety affect your interaction with your
loved one in their final moments?

HEARTBROKEN

At some point, often much later than you'd think, a loved one's
choice to have MAID changes from a philosophical 'better way
forward' to a realization that this will result in their final breath,
their actual death. This can be uncomfortable or even frightening
to think about, particularly when reality sets in on the day.

Cathy shares how the proceedings on her husband's MAID day
left her sad and heartbroken.

Cathy

I woke up that morning and listened to Gary's laboured breathing
as he lay beside me.

This can't be happening, I thought. I reflected on all the mornings we
had greeted the day together. *How can it all be ending today?* It was
too horrible to face so, while in the back of my mind I was
screaming, on the surface I pretended it wasn't happening.

I did what I needed to do. I got up and made coffee, did a couple
of loads of laundry, and tidied the house. By that time, Gary was
up and sitting in his Lazy Boy. He was in a world of his own, but I
couldn't stand to be shut out. I interrupted his reverie as he stared
out the window and asked what he was thinking.

"Flying high and landing safe" was the answer from this man
who had piloted his own plane for years. That hit me like a punch
in the stomach as the reality of what I was trying to deny surfaced,
and the horrible truth rushed in.

170

MAID Day

He was so brave that it broke my heart. From the beginning, he had never complained and had faced his fate like he'd faced his life, with dignity, integrity and strength. In a way, this made it harder for me. *How could I live without this wonderful man?*

I sat across from him, dreading the knock on the door that would signal the arrival of the MAID team. My mind raced as I searched for some way to stop the process, to protect him from it. But we had already been there, done that and had arrived at the only alternative that would end his suffering and give him peace.

I cringed when that knock inevitably came. With his daughters, Amanda and Julia, and the MAID team, Cindy and Ram, we went into the back room that overlooks the lake behind our house. Cindy began to set up the vials and potions behind Gary's chair where he couldn't see them.

"What's taking so long?" Gary asked, in direct contrast to my silent pleading to make this stop because I couldn't bear it. His eyes darted from side to side in confusion. I softly asked him to look at me, which seemed to steady him. I became the last person he saw on this earth until the light slowly faded from his eyes. There are no words to describe the pain I felt as I held his hand for a few more minutes and then gently closed his eyes with my fingertips.

How Do You Feel?
Were you heartbroken? What did that feel like?

Chapter 6

Resentful

MAID day can bring out feelings of resentment towards other family members, the medical system, and even our loved one. How did things progress so quickly? Is it really true that today is the day? How can we be expected to be ready for something like this?

Nikki shares how she hoped for reconciliation on her father's MAID day, and how she wrote the letter from her father that she wished she'd received but did not.

Nikki

I remember waking up thinking, *Okay, this is the day. My dad is going to die in a few hours.* I put on my armour for the day, hoping for magic but preparing for pain: leather pants, high tops, and a black plaid shirt.

I dropped my two young children off at school and then stopped to pick up pastries for my family members — the ones who had hardly been present for the last three years of hell. I steeled myself, hoping my mother and brother would follow my directions and not upset my father. I prayed they would behave, that there wouldn't be a fight or terrible words exchanged. As always, I was worrying about holding space for everyone else. *What about me?*

The little girl in me longed for a deathbed reconciliation with my father. I wanted a Hallmark movie ending where my dad apologized to me and thanked me for everything I had done for him, and my family acknowledged all of my sacrifices and hard work for my dad.

But there was no magic — not from my dad and not from my family members. Only pain.

I looked down into his gray face and saw he was gone.

MAID Day

The doctor announced the time of his death.

The words he never told me and the apology he wasn't able to give me were also gone.

It hurt like a huge gaping wound in my chest. It stung. It ached. I felt empty. My armour hadn't protected me.

If only he could have told me the things I'd so desperately needed to hear…

Nicolina, my darling daughter.

I love you so much. You are my pride and joy. You are kind, compassionate, smart, strong and courageous. I could never have imagined having such a beautiful soul for a child. You helped me so much and I was terrible to you. I know that. I know that my dependency on alcohol made me miserable to be around. I know some of my actions are unforgettable and maybe even unforgivable to the sweet, innocent child my actions hurt. I wish I could take all the pain and bad memories away. I wish that all you could remember of me were the tender moments when I was able to express my love. It was so hard for me to do that, and I regret that I didn't work harder at it.

I wish I had said kinder things to you. I hate that I have made my baby girl hurt so much. I failed as a dad. I may have provided for you financially, but I failed to provide for you where it mattered most. I didn't make you feel safe. I didn't make you feel unconditionally loved. You deserved that. You needed that. I'm sorry.

I am so proud of you. I am proud of the man you have chosen and the family you have created and all the things you have done with your life. You are MORE than enough. I am so lucky you are my daughter. You were and are and always will be the biggest gift of my life. You ended my suffering, even though I made you suffer so much. I didn't deserve your love after all I put you through. And yet, you stood by my side and made sure I got everything I needed. My dear, darling daughter. Thank you.

I don't want you to hurt anymore. You deserve to feel all the joy and happiness you bring to others.

Take care of yourself. Take care of my granddaughters. They are so lucky to have you as their mom. I know they will be ok because they have you as their mom.

I love them and I love you and I'm sorry.

Thank you.

Dad.

How Do You Feel?

Did you feel resentful on MAID day? Who or what did you resent?

SADNESS

Sadness is the one emotion that pretty much everyone can relate to when it comes to surviving the death of a loved one. We feel it in our hearts and in our bodies — an acute heaviness that presses down on us, taking our breath away at times, producing uncontrollable tears at others. A kind of strange inertia sets in when sadness takes over. We find ourselves staring at walls without seeing them, of going through the motions of living but not being present. All we want is what we can't have — our loved one back.

Bobbie shares how sadness permeated the day her husband Bob had MAID.

Bobbie

The day is finally here, and I wish we had picked a time in the morning. Waiting is overwhelmingly painful and the sadness in my heart makes me feel like I will not survive the day. We have talked and talked and now there is nothing of importance left to say. The sun is shining, and we drive to our favourite spot. I wish I could stop weeping. I know my tears are making it more difficult for my husband, but even the sun feels like an unbearable weight on my shoulders. Bob tells me again that he wants me to find joy in my life and that he loves me. There is no magic in this. Bob has been sick for so long. I know he is tired and ready to die. But I don't want him to die. I'm not ready to live without him. I am so sad that this is the direction our lives have taken.

His sister comes and they have a private talk. Sadness is everywhere. The nurses and the MAID doctor are all very kind and thoughtful. They have a hard time putting the needle in Bob's arm and I see him wince. My heart breaks some more. I realize this is the last time he will feel pain. He hates needles, and he has had so many in his 23 years with Parkinson's Disease. He moves to his chair, which I have turned towards the garden. The window is open for his spirit to soar. His sister takes one hand, and I the other. They administer the final medication, and he looks at me and says, "you have been an amazing wife and I love you." And then he is gone…

OMG it is too soon.

I also want to die. I know instantly that we didn't plan this correctly. We should be together. The sadness is crushing my body. My heart actually feels like it is breaking. I am more alone than I have ever been in my life, and a part of me has gone with him. I know he is at peace after so long, but there is no peace for me. I can see now that I will never be the same. I don't want to believe he's gone.

How Do You Feel?
Write about your own sadness. How does it feel in your body?

175

Chapter 6

ISOLATED

Many people can relate to watching a loved one die, but very few understand how it feels to be present at a loved one's MAID death. MAID is still so new that many of us may know only a handful of people who have been involved with it—and maybe none at all. Often, we must cope in isolation with the pain we experienced watching our loved one choose to die.

Emily shares how isolated she felt when her wife's MAID Day arrived.

Emily

I only had 17 hours to process that Veronica was going to die. Veronica was my world, and I wanted to be the one to be with her for the remaining time she had on this earth.

She had decided that she only wanted the people who were directly in her life to know about her decision to have MAID. She told me, her children and her medical team and asked us not to tell anyone else. I'm very close to my family and it was hard for me to not be able to share it with them. I wanted to keep this enormous secret because of the love and respect I had for Veronica, but I also wanted my family to be there with me to hold my hand.

This choice was hers and I didn't want her to leave on a negative note, so I honoured her request. But sitting beside her and holding her hand when it was time was probably the hardest thing I have ever experienced in my life. Veronica was my soul mate, my best friend, my life, and to not have anyone beside me, holding me, being there for me after she died was devastating. I felt so empty, lost, and defeated. After she stopped breathing and her heart stopped, I felt like my heart had also stopped. Veronica was the spark in my life, and I instantly felt alone. There were nine of us in the room when she died, but I didn't notice anyone else. I only saw her lifeless body sitting in front of me. I couldn't let go of her hand for what seemed like hours.

How Do You Feel?
Have you felt isolated in your experience with MAID?

LOVE

Helping a loved one carry out their wishes — even when those wishes involve ending their lives with MAID — is the ultimate act of love. We are supposed to put aside our sadness and grief and hold space for our loved one. We are supposed to honour their choice and support them.

This act of love is both agonizing and liberating. At the end, we can call upon our love to comfort our loved one and to keep ourselves strong, or we can call upon their love for us, to comfort ourselves in our own loss.

Cynthia and Carol share how love carried them through MAID day.

Cynthia
My husband's love for me, and for our kids was evident in every decision he made. From the moment he was diagnosed with brain cancer, his singular focus was on living well while he could. He wanted a good time, not the most time, and threw himself into living his last year well, with and for our young children and me. His most important words to me shortly after his devastating diagnosis were "don't waste too much time being sad for me. You are too young and too wonderful to not share your life with someone. Promise me you will find happiness again."

Chapter 6

My husband, who had been too scared of the doctor's office to get a vasectomy, braved an awake craniotomy and daily trips to the radiation centre, to give us time with him to say goodbye.

He spent the week between diagnosis and surgery building a master file of every log-in and password he could think of so I would be able to manage our affairs. While on chemo, he rationed his daily energy to be awake and available to cuddle our kids to sleep at night. He put his fierce independence aside and learned to accept help from friends and strangers alike so the kids could keep participating in their activities. He attended their soccer games and Christmas concerts, with 47 staples in his skull and in a wheelchair at times, and held his head high and proud, beaming his best half-smile from the front row.

He swallowed his pride and agreed to me hiring a babysitter for the kids (and him) so I could have a break from caregiving when he wasn't well enough to be the only adult at home. He let me bring a helper on our family vacation so we could all enjoy one another's company. He decided to die and not pursue alternative treatments or clinical trials because he wanted our kids to remember him well. He wanted us to hurry up and get on with living the rest of our lives. He wanted us to be happy, even though he wouldn't be around to see us living happily.

My husband didn't think dying at home would be a great idea, but he agreed to it when I told him it would be better for our kids. He beamed with gratitude when he saw the beautiful space we had created in our guest room for him to die comfortably, surrounded by happy memories and the kids' artwork. He told our children that he loved them and he let them see his tears as they said goodbye, "you are the best daddy ever," "I will miss your cuddles," "you are so smart and hardworking," "I will never forget you," "I will miss you."

I held my husband in my arms as he died, knowing that his love for us was fierce and steadfast. I felt him drift off to sleep, his head resting on my shoulder. He had done every single thing possible to make sure we knew how loved we were. I heard his breathing change and then stop as life slipped out of his body, but his love remained. It's in the memories we carry with us, the lessons he taught us, and his love is infused in the spirit of the beautiful children we made together.

Carol

I was alone with Mom and her two wonderful nurses when she passed. The family had spent the afternoon crowded into her tiny care home room, laughing, singing, and playing with Mom's six-month-old great-granddaughter. We even took a family photo in which we included pictures of my brother and my dad, both of whom had already passed.

When the nurses arrived, the family went out to the lobby, and it was just Mom and me. While we waited for the nurses to get set up, I told her about our plan to go out to dinner 'after.' She always wanted to be included in everything and so quickly replied, "Can I come?" I laughed and said "Sure, Mom, if that's what you want!" and then she remembered and laughed too. I'm so grateful that I saw that twinkle in her eye just moments before the end.

And then the IV went in, and I said, "I love you." The words were not enough to prevent me from falling headlong into the darkest, most bereft few minutes of my life. Nothing else comes close to the feeling of complete and total shock that enveloped me when I realized she was gone. I cried then — my heartbreak so intense that even the nurses had tears in their eyes.

I am blessed to be loved by several people in my life, but no one could ever love me like Mom did. How was I going to continue without her?

Chapter 6

How Do You Feel?

Were you able to express your love and feel your loved one's love for you on MAID day?

TRANSCENDENCE

Death is the ultimate human mystery. We may have beliefs, but we can never know exactly what will happen when we die until we experience it ourselves. To watch a loved one die brings us as close to death as we will get until it's our turn. For some, MAID is a transcendent experience, resulting in the end of pain for our loved one and the beginning of peace for them and us.

Dave L. shares how he felt watching his beloved wife Annie pass.

Dave L.

On the morning of Annie's MAID procedure, Annie was still pain free, but her energy wasn't quite as high as it had been the day before. After breakfast, she said that she would go lie on my bed while I got her room ready for the doctor, who was due to arrive around 1:30 pm.

I happened to open the vanity drawer in the bathroom and found a note from Annie that read, "When I'm gone, bleach the drain." Annie hated when the drains began to smell, but whenever I tried to get rid of the smell by pouring bleach down them, it would trigger Annie's asthma. It was a lose-lose situation that had been a constant issue throughout our relationship.

I took the note and went to lie with her on the bed, where we laughed and talked a little about this and that. She was still pain free.

The doctor arrived on time and the nurse was late, but eventually everything was ready. "Do you still want to die?" the doctor asked. "I do," said Annie, with no hesitation whatsoever.

As the first infusion began, Annie's eyelids began to flutter, and she whispered, "I love you," then smiled and added, "Don't forget the bleach."

Her death was as peaceful as she had wished. There was no physical pain and as I held her hand, I experienced the release of the deep mental and emotional pain that had held her in its thrall for most of her life. Twenty minutes after the procedure began, the MAID provider pronounced Annie dead and left me holding Annie's hand. Her body was dead, but Annie was still in residence, and it wasn't till someone called from downstairs an hour or so later that I turned away for a moment. When I turned back, I could feel that she had left. What did not change was the connection that Annie and I had shared in life and deepened in the months before her death. It did not end on MAID day and has not diminished with the passage of time.

How Do You Feel?

Did you feel transcendence watching your loved one receive MAID? What did it feel like for you?

Chapter 6

PEACEFUL

We often say that a person who has died is finally at peace. This peace can also extend to those of us who have supported our loved one through MAID. After all the heartbreak and turmoil that can accompany the lead-up to MAID, we can also finally find peace.

Andrée shares how she felt at peace when she was with her daughter on MAID day.

Andrée

MAID day, my last day together with my eldest daughter, Kim. Her husband, her sister and I spent the day with her at the hospital, where she had chosen to die. Some people, like her in-laws, came and went but the three of us were with her all day. I felt at peace with her decision to have MAID. I spent this day feeling calm, the stress of the past few months behind me. Kim's journey with cancer was coming to an end. She was ready and so was I. I had no doubt that this was the right decision, and I was at peace with it.

We shared memories. We laughed. We cried. She took the time to speak to each of us individually. One of the things Kim and I talked about was death. I reassured her that she was going to be with her father, who had died 12 years earlier. This was a comforting thought for both of us. I imagined her father and my parents waiting for her on the other side. I felt less heartbroken, knowing she wouldn't be alone. Somehow, it made losing her easier to accept.

Kim wanted to make sure I knew she loved me, and she asked me to write down her maid of honour speech for when her sister would get married. When Kim spoke with her sister, she made sure to discuss my sixtieth birthday, which was two years away, so that she could be part of my celebration. It was a very calm and peaceful day. I wouldn't have to worry about her pain or watch her die slowly. She would finally be at peace.

When the time came, I kissed Kim and held her hand while her husband held her other hand. We watched her peacefully fall asleep and her pain disappear.

How Do You Feel?
Was MAID day peaceful for you and your loved one? How did you feel knowing that your loved was finally at peace?

HONOURED

Being invited to witness someone's final moments can be an honour and a privilege. To have the choice to participate without obligation or assumption can be a touching experience.

Shannon shares what witnessing her friend Wendy's death taught her.

Shannon

Wendy allowed me to witness her struggle, but also to find peace in the most vulnerable and intimate transition of her life. I felt honoured to be invited to be by her side the day she died to watch the art of dying magnificently play out before me.

Wendy showed me how beautiful life can be just by the way she lived it. She taught me how significant a brief moment can be, how sitting in silence can be more meaningful and stimulating than lengthy, drawn-out conversations.

She taught me the importance of showing up and how challenging letting go can be, how difficult it is to discern if a piece of your life needs to change or grow or just to go. It was an

Chapter 6

honour to learn these lessons from such a humble teacher and friend.

How Do You Feel?
How did you feel being invited to participate in your loved one's medically assisted death?

GRATEFUL

So many emotions swirl around us on MAID day—some comforting and some challenging, some painful and some joyful. For many of us, feeling gratitude for our loved one's life and for the peacefulness of their passing helps ease the sadness. Daimhin shares the gratitude she felt when her dad died, happy and at peace.

Daimhin

I don't remember how much I slept the night before my dad died. We had only found out the previous day that there was a doctor available at 9:30 am to perform the procedure. While it is what we wanted, and my dad was way past the point he ever hoped to get to, it still felt like a punch to the gut. It seemed too soon, with no time to prepare.

I woke up that August morning and for a couple seconds thought perhaps it had all been just a dream. Then reality hit me like a ton of bricks. Today was the day the man I knew and loved so much, my father, would die.

His pain had been getting worse and worse and he had become distant. On the morning of MAID day, my mom wanted him to be completely pain free, so she upped his pain meds a little bit, which made him pretty loopy. But for the first time in a long time, he seemed happy and out of pain.

We sat around the hospital bed that occupied our living room and shared our last morning with him. He was so high. He was imagining himself fly-fishing and I could see his hands reeling in a fish. He was calm, and I could tell he was at peace.

As we sat together, he spoke in a way I hadn't heard in months. The intonations in his voice were more recognizable, and he was smiling more and more as we talked. I can't remember what we talked about, but I do remember the flood of relief I had as we sat there, spending our last time together as a family. I had been so worried and stressed that this last morning would be traumatizing, sad, and disappointing. The tightness in my body melted away seeing him free of pain, speaking and laughing with us. In that moment, I realized that this would become my final memory with my dad, and that it was a good one. The months leading up to this day had been horrible and upsetting, so having this peaceful and happy moment at the very end is something I will be forever grateful for.

My grandma, uncle and aunt, as well as our friends who are more like family, spent the last couple of hours of my dad's life sitting with him, saying goodbye and sharing memories. It was the hardest and saddest day of my life, but I am so grateful that all these important people were able to share his last morning with him.

When the doctor arrived, she was wearing a floral jumpsuit and she was what I would describe as sunshine in human form. She immediately went to my dad and spoke to him with such understanding, empathy, and kindness. I don't think she will ever know how grateful I am to her. She was able to soften the blow of 'the day I lost my father' just with her kindness and sincerity.

185

As she started to inject the medications, my dad said, "I hope I don't snore too loudly" and then fell asleep and snored very loudly until his heart stopped.

How Do You Feel?

Were you left with good memories of your loved one's death? Write about how you felt during the last hours.

WHAT'S YOUR STORY?

If your loved one has already had MAID, then the stories in this chapter will likely resonate. If you are preparing to say goodbye, you might have found these stories helpful. Take some time to process your own emotions, knowing they may be different from those of our storytellers.

Listed below are each of the emotions presented by our storytellers. Consider which ones resonate with you and then use them to help you explore and honour your own emotions. Take this opportunity to think and write about *everything* that you are or have been feeling.

- Numb
- Resigned
- Nervous
- Apprehensive
- Heartbroken
- Resentful
- Sadness

- Isolated
- Love
- Transcendence
- Honoured
- Peaceful
- Grateful

How Do You Feel?

Which emotions and stories resonate with you?

Which emotions do not resonate with you?

What emotions did you feel that were not included?

Has anything that you've felt during your journey surprised you?

Is there something you wish you had said to your loved one, or that they had said to you?

CHAPTER 7 -

AFTER MAID

Absence is a house so vast that inside you will pass
through its walls and hang pictures on the air. —
Pablo Neruda

After our loved one has passed, we face entering a new chapter in our lives without them. Now what? How do we move forward? Where's the playbook for people who have supported someone through MAID and must now carry on living?

In some cases, grief mingles with gratitude that our loved one is at peace, or relief that we are freed from worry and the stress of being a caregiver. Emotions are mixed, just as they have been throughout this entire journey. One day we may be calm and accepting, and the next we can be plunged into a black hole of sorrow or regret.

Our storytellers share how they felt and how they coped in the days following their loved one receiving MAID.

SADNESS

Sadness permeates the soul, erasing our edges as we collapse in on ourselves. The emotional pain drains us of energy. Some days, it's all we can do to get out of bed and face the day. Sadness empties us. It destroys our incentive to do anything more than stare and remember.

Dave B. shares how he coped with the debilitating sadness of losing his wife.

Dave B.

What do you feel when the person you love most in the world, and the person who loved you as no one else on Earth ever will again, leaves you forever?

Annie died on the living room sofa, and she wanted to stay there overnight. I slept in our bed, alone for the first time in many years. In the morning, men came from the funeral home, zipped her into a body bag, and took her body away. As they drove off, I wondered who I was now, no longer part of a golden couple. I felt immense, immeasurable sadness that our life together was over.

How could I go on without her? No more morning teas. No more hugs, no more kisses. No more intimacy at such a deep level with anyone else, for the rest of my life. Being half of Annie and Dave was the most essential part of my life. It's who I was. I would miss that beyond belief. I could not really grasp what Annie's death meant to me.

Some time afterwards, I talked to a friend whose brother had just had MAID. She said it was terrible to lose her brother, but to lose her husband was unimaginable. That is the perfect word.

Two years on, I still have difficulty imagining the unimaginable loss of the love of my life.

Chapter 7

How Do You Feel?

How did sadness manifest for you after MAID day? How did your body feel?

BEREFT

The word *bereft* perfectly describes the terrible emptiness that follows a loved one's MAID death. All the light in the world seems to have dimmed, leaving us to drift alone in an ocean of emptiness. To be bereft means to be deprived of something that we love — and that something is time with our loved one that we'll never have again.

Robin and Carol share how they felt bereft following the deaths of their parents.

Robin

We had only a week's notice of my dad's MAID date, and despite wanting to stretch it out, to have as much time with him as possible, the date came very quickly. I felt as though I had been slingshot into some weird space— from the 'before,' where I knew about MAID just as a concept, to the 'after,' where I had been through MAID with someone and had to figure out how to process it. It felt like I was alone on a desolate landscape that very few people had seen.

A loved one's death is never easy, but my dad's death through MAID felt particularly lonely. I hadn't managed to find much in the way of resources before he died, but before she left the room the doctor who provided MAID to my dad gave us a pamphlet.

That single sheet did have a couple of helpful resources on it, but it felt flimsy next to the weight of what had happened. My dad had been ill and had opted to end his life with medical assistance, which, until a few months prior, I hadn't actually realized was legal in Canada. I had accepted my dad's decision and done my best to explain it to my kids. I was in the room with my dad, and I held his hand as he died. One minute he was talking to us, and then the doctor put something in his IV and he was gone.

It was an event so significant that no pamphlet could possibly begin to address it.

When thinking about that time, one word comes immediately to mind: bereft. We often hear that in the context of death, but it has another meaning as well: deprived of or lacking something.

I still shake my head when I think about that pamphlet. My need at the time was so great and that pamphlet didn't come close to touching the black hole I existed in after my dad's MAID death. I needed support and it was just...lacking.

Carol

In the moments after my mom's death, all the love I felt for her burst forth in a torrent of tears more intense than any I had ever experienced.

The world went dark. As I stared at her lifeless body, I felt an overwhelming emptiness — like nothing could ever be the same for me again. I wanted to share my tears with Mom, to let her know just how much I loved her. I'd never let her see me cry, never let her know the depth of my love for her. I'd kept a stiff upper lip all through the weeks and days leading up to MAID day — cracking jokes, being helpful and efficient, maintaining a relentless cheerfulness. I never once broke down in front of her because I didn't want her to regret her decision. And now it was too late to let her know how I really felt.

The sight of her slumped in her chair, all life extinguished, will never leave me. One moment she was with me, her eyes sparkling, her determination strong to the end, and the next moment, she was gone. I stared at her face, but it wasn't the face of my mother anymore. It was collapsed and quiet and just...empty.

I wanted to scream at the nurses to bring her back. This whole thing had been a huge mistake. *How could Mom do this? She shouldn't have left me. Why did I let her go? What kind of a daughter was I to have let her go?*

My head knew she'd done what she wanted to do, but my heart kept telling me that maybe I could have stopped her, that maybe I could have kept her with me for longer. I will never forget how bereft I felt sitting in that small room holding her hand, feeling no warmth or life, knowing that my wonderful mother who had always been my greatest support was gone forever.

How Do You Feel?

Did you feel bereft after your loved one died? Write about your experience of feeling bereft?

OVERWHELMED

The reality of MAID can be overwhelming. All the planning and preparation, the long talks and long good-byes, suddenly fall by the wayside. The crushing finality of death can leave us feeling overwhelmed, struggling to find a way to put one foot in front of the other.

Daimhin shares how she reacted following the death of her father.

After MAID

Daimhin

The hours after my dad died were a blur. I know who was sitting where in the room when the doctor announced his time of death. My mom was holding his right hand, I was holding his left hand, my sister was beside me, and my grandma behind me.

I am not sure how long we sat there. I know that toasts were made in his name and my mom stayed by his side longer than anyone else.

The people from the funeral home arrived. My mom grabbed my sister and me, and pulled our heads together in a huddle so neither of us could watch as they lifted my dad's lifeless body into the green velvet body bag.

In that moment, forehead to forehead, our eyes squeezed tight and holding onto each other for dear life, I realized that it was just the three of us now. We were no longer a family of four, but a unit of three. The intensity of this moment stunned me. I was reeling from the grief of watching my dad die and feeling the gut punching reality of only four arms wrapped around me instead of the six I had been used to for my entire life. I could barely handle the barrage of emotions. The relief of him being out of pain, the emptiness of losing my dad, the trauma of seeing his lifeless body, the crushing reality that my life was forever changed, made me weak in the knees.

I didn't feel like I could continue living. I had to actively try to stay alive and remind myself to breathe. I was sure that all the emotions I was feeling would literally kill me if I let them. It was exhausting to be alive that day. It seemed as though I needed all my focus just to keep my heart beating and my lungs breathing.

How Do You Feel?

What contributed to you feeling overwhelmed when your loved one died? What were some things you needed to do to cope with the magnitude of your feelings?

EXHAUSTED

For many, the lead-up to MAID day is a whirlwind of activity. Not only do you want to 'be there' for your loved one, you likely need to attend to practical matters such as scheduling and making sure your loved one's wishes are met. You may also need to organize visits from friends and relatives, some of whom may also need support. You must be everything to everyone and everywhere at once when all you really want to do is be with your loved one. No wonder you might be overwhelmed by exhaustion when MAID is finally over.

Cynthia shares how exhausted she felt having to cope with the needs of her children and the demands of celebrations such as Halloween and Christmas following her husband's death.

Cynthia

Halloween was six weeks after my husband died and I was exhausted. In the past, we had planned family costumes with themes and cute make-up. It was the only holiday when we would abandon our criticisms of overly commercialized celebrations and spend more money than necessary on coloured lights, music and spooky yard items from the Halloween pop-up shop. I loved making these silly memories.

The first Halloween without my husband, I was annoyed that I had to participate at all. It seemed like so much work. I wished I could get excited with my kids, but honestly, I just wanted it to be over so I could stop feeling guilty about not having the energy to go shopping, or dig out the box of decorations, or climb the ladder to hang them, or plan a party, or smile. I barely had enough energy for the daily routines. I found planning meals and doing laundry damn near impossible. I had lowered my standards for pretty much everything. The clutter in my house was mounting, the chores list was growing, and my energy was depleted earlier and earlier each day. Halloween was just one more damn thing making my to-do list longer, and my feelings of failure bigger. It was overwhelming and I was so tired.

My children regularly came home from school cranky and SO NEEDY. I felt constantly torn between their increased needs, my own needs, and the mounting work around the house. Well meaning, but contradictory advice rang in my head and confused me.

"How are the kids?... the poor kids."

"What are you doing for yourself?"

"The kids, they really need this first milestone to be special. They need YOU."

"You can't pour from an empty cup."

It didn't help that as soon as Halloween was over, it was time for Christmas. My kids were excited for the familiar Christmas traditions, unaware of the volume of additional work that Christmas required, not to mention the emotional landmines that lay in wait for all three of us. I was too tired to make Christmas happen on my own, too tired to fight with my kids about why we weren't getting a real tree, and just too tired to care.

I tried to muster some enthusiasm and participate in fun activities with my kids, but mostly I just felt guilty that I wanted to be by myself, without the responsibility of being a single parent. I wanted to stay in bed all day, go for long walks, and have some peace and quiet. I was tired of trying to figure out how to be a grieving wife AND a mom of grieving kids.

How Do You Feel?

Did you feel exhausted after your loved one died? Take some time to write about it.

ABANDONED

Our loved one is gone, and we've been abandoned to face the future without them. It's impossible! We can't be expected to carry on, can we? And yet, we must. There are so many things to attend to—a whole new landscape of obligations opens up. And sometimes, we find ourselves abandoned by the people we needed most to depend upon. Alone, we must attend to bittersweet tasks such as gathering up our loved one's possessions and packing away their clothes.

Bobbie shares how alone she felt following the death of her husband, and Brittney shares how she felt abandoned when she had to step up and cope on her own with the tasks that needed doing after the death of her mother.

Bobbie

After Bob died, I felt so alone. We were always together, a pair, but now, I was by myself. I was waiting to feel something more than profound loss. I was hoping that I would be happy that Bob was no longer suffering, but instead I just felt abandoned. I couldn't empty the dishwasher or remember to eat or read more than a paragraph. I was just surviving...and wishing that I wasn't. Nothing felt important or urgent without Bob there to notice.

After MAID

I wanted to do this grief thing well, so I called to speak to a therapist, thinking I was being proactive. My family had all died, abandoning me long ago, and I was never close to Bob's sister, even though I'd tried to be. I had endless friends, so I was not alone, but it felt like only my elder dog was really 100% there for me. I instantly adored the funeral director, George. He told me kindly what to expect in the days ahead. He came three times and stayed a couple of hours each time, helping me more than he could possibly have known.

Then my girlfriend called from Florida and at the end she asked what I had planned for the rest of the day. I hung up the phone and the tears started and have never stopped. I had nothing planned, not for that day or any other day in the future. I had no one to come home to and share the silly stories of my days with. I had been Bob's wife and caregiver for so long that I no longer had any other purpose. Bob had been sick for a long time, but I'd never given in to thinking about him leaving me, about my life without him. I had no desire or motivation to find something meaningful to do, so I sat there in my chair just waiting for darkness to come and the day to end. I only moved from the chair when the dog needed something. I was alone. I felt abandoned.

Brittney

I was a mess in the days following my mom's passing. I wanted to scream, cry and pack up my stuff and take off somewhere far away to try and process what the hell had just happened.

I slept at my parent's house for a week following my mom's death to better assist with the funeral arrangements, planning and paperwork. I also wanted to be with my stepdad, who is more like a dad to me. There was comfort in knowing that he had lost her too. It felt eerie at their place. All my mom's things were exactly how she had left them. I could still smell her and hear her voice as I sat looking out the window at her hummingbird feeder. It was

Chapter 7

both heartbreaking and comforting. It's hard to describe how surreal it was. I knew she was gone, but it felt like she could have been on holiday and would be back in just a few days.

Even though I was surrounded by family and had the support of my friends, I felt extremely alone. The world kept moving but I wasn't ready to move with it. I started wearing my mom's flip flops, which were a size too big, and continued to wear them for the remainder of the summer. I guess it was another way for me to feel close to my mom.

My family was obviously very distraught during this time but also had their own families to take care of. I somehow managed to take the reins and help tie up the loose ends. At 32, I had never had to deal with anything like this. Finalizing my mom's funeral plans was a pretty shitty job! I felt abandoned. *Why did I get the short end of the stick?* Sure, there were people I could ask for help, but they were grieving too. I did not want to burden anyone.

The worst task was unpacking my mom's hospital bag. I was dreading doing this. I felt my body temperature rise and tried not to cry or scream as I opened the bag in the spare bedroom. I held back tears as I stared at her clothes hanging in the closet, as if she was going to wear the items again. I wanted her to walk through the front door, happy and healthy again. I wanted one of my sisters to do this crappy job, or at least do it with me. I put her toothbrush back in the bathroom, her sweater back in her bedroom and her purse in the spare room closet as if she was coming back. I was not ready to throw the items out, no way in hell. It was one of the hardest things I've had to do. *But someone had to do it, right?*

How Do You Feel?

Did you feel alone or abandoned after MAID day? How did people in your life help you (or not)?

EMPTY

In the lead-up to MAID day, we may try to anticipate how we'll act after our loved one dies, but the reality is that we can have no idea how we will feel. Instead of feeling a gamut of emotions from grief to anger to relief, we may suddenly feel a deep and seemingly infinite emptiness.

Cathy shares the darkness that overwhelmed her following the MAID death of her husband.

Cathy

In the days following Gary's death, there were times when everything came to a screeching halt, and I was plunged into a darkness I had never experienced before. A darkness I was unprepared for and defenseless against, where my only choice was surrender. I let it wash over me — this hollow feeling of being at the bottom of a well with no sound, light or colour, shut off from the land of the living, alone and afraid.

The darkness came with flashbacks of Gary's death which drove home that he wasn't coming back, and I would be missing him to the end of my days. You would think that taking care of him for a year and a half would have prepared me for the finality of it all … but it didn't. I was so involved in keeping him alive for as long as possible that death was mostly just a concept.

In those early days, the darkness was my reality from the moment I woke up until I finally drifted into a fitful sleep. I desperately tried to regain a sense of control. I felt devastated and hollow every time I looked at Gary's empty Lazy Boy or opened his closet full of clothes. I threw myself into sorting through his things and either getting rid of them or putting them where they didn't lay in wait for me.

I couldn't get it together enough to feed myself, so when a couple of friends asked me to meet them for dinner at a restaurant, I agreed. It was raining that evening and we had just gone off daylight savings time so the dreariness outside mimicked the way I felt inside.

Our meal began okay, with them asking what they could do to help. We ordered and the food came quickly. The conversation turned to my friends, and they innocently went on about their families, work and lives. Suddenly I couldn't breathe as I realized that the normal things they were discussing would never be normal for me again.

As I felt myself plunging into that cold dark well, I stood up and ran out of the restaurant, leaving my worried friends behind. I drove quickly, seeking refuge and comfort in the home where Gary and I had lived happily and shared our lives. It was quiet and dark, and I found no comfort there. The echoes of those earlier times magnified what I had lost, and I felt more alone and emptier than ever.

How Do You Feel?

Can you relate to feeling empty and alone after your loved one had MAID? How did this feel for you?

After MAID

Lost

When you have been the principal caregiver of your loved one — sometimes for many years — you will likely feel lost when suddenly all the tasks that had filled your days are no longer necessary. How do you fill your time? You may feel both restless and exhausted at the same time, not knowing how you can possibly find your way back to a life without your loved one.

Andrée shares how lost she felt after her daughter's MAID.

Andrée

I held it together until Kim's celebration of life. In the elevator going from the service to the reception, I finally broke down and cried. All of a sudden, I realized that it was over. Kim was really gone, forever.

Now what do I do? I felt so lost. No more doctors' appointments to take her to, no more treatments to sit through, no more hospital visits together, no more calls asking for my help with this or that, no more worrying whether she was eating enough, no more checking on her.

I didn't know what to do with myself. We were at our summer place so that I could take care of myself. I was so tired but so restless at the same time. I didn't know how to grieve for my daughter. I wasn't supposed to be grieving my child. She was supposed to outlive me.

I missed her so much. There was a big hole in my life that didn't seem possible to fill. I used to call Kim's cell phone just to hear her voice, wishing I could talk to her. I felt so lost without her.

Kim and I had not been very close and did not always get along when she was growing up. She was not an easy teenager. Until she got sick, she was so independent; we didn't have the kind of relationship I have with my other daughter where we talk or text all time. But when she got sick, I was the only one she wanted by her side. When she died, I missed seeing her all the time and our new closeness. I mourned all the things I knew she wouldn't be able to do in her life. I think of her every day, and I wonder what her life would look like now. Would we have remained close? In my heart, I think we would have found a way for me to respect her independence and still stay close.

How Do You Feel?

Did you feel lost after your loved one's MAID? How did you cope with the sudden void in your life?

ANGRY

While acknowledging that our loved one has the right to make their own decisions, we may not be able to help feeling angry. How could they do this to us? How could they leave us? None of this is fair! Anger is the flip side of fear — and is often the result of us being terrified of facing the future without our loved one. Sometimes, it's easier to channel our emotions into anger than to allow the fear to control us.

Anger may also be directed at other people in our lives — people who do not understand the MAID journey and may even object to it. Their comments can be very hurtful and justifiably spark anger.

Emily shares how she felt anger as a result of her wife's MAID decision, and Elizabeth shares the anger she experienced in response to some people's reactions to her mother's MAID.

Emily

I never understood why Veronica didn't want to tell anyone about her decision to have MAID. It made me angry that she left it up to me and her children. I had so much love and respect for her that I had honoured her request. I thought it was the least I could do since I couldn't imagine what she was going through, but as time went on, I felt more and more angry with her. I'm not usually an angry person, so these feelings surprised me. I was angry that she pushed me away and didn't spend more time with me at the end, and angry that she hadn't been more considerate of me and my feelings.

Veronica's parents came to our apartment an hour or two after she died. *Why didn't she want to tell her parents that she chose MAID?* I thought to myself. I was worried about how to tell them, how they would react and what they would say when they found out that I knew about her choice in advance. I was worried that they would ask me why I hadn't told them, and I was angry at Veronica for putting the responsibility of telling them on me. I had just watched the love of my life die, I was devastated, and then I had to figure out a way to tell her parents. I didn't think they would see me the same way once they knew I'd withheld this information from them. *Why hadn't she just told her family herself?*

Elizabeth

When a friend of mine told me that "only God can decide when someone should die," I found myself getting very angry. I wondered if they had ever witnessed a loved one suffering. My heart raced and I wanted to scream and yell and ask them if they have a heart, but I fought to remain composed.

When various friends said that they were praying for me, or keeping me in their thoughts and prayers, I forced myself not to roll my eyes, and pushed down the sudden urge to laugh and tell them what I really thought, which is: "I believe in what I can see. You might even call me an atheist." I wished they understood that I was struggling and needed a shoulder to lean on. Prayers felt useless to me. They may as well have done nothing. The result in my mind would have been identical.

How I would have loved to believe that my mom and dad went somewhere beautiful after they died, and that I would get to see them again someday. It probably would have made their deaths and the MAID aftermath easier.

Another friend told me, "my mother was a coward for choosing to die, and that she shouldn't have had the right to make the choice to end her life using MAID." To be clear, she didn't want to die. She still had grandchildren to watch grow up and people to love, but her body was telling her it was time. I really could have used less judgment and more support. I was very angry that someone who didn't know my mom was judging her and our family for supporting her choice. It would have been far more helpful to be kind.

How Do You Feel?

Did you experience anger after your loved one's MAID? Who or what sparked your anger?

NOSTALGIC

One of the many tasks we may have to do following the passing of our loved one is sorting through their belongings. The process can be a cathartic one that brings forth a wide range of emotions, from sadness and grief to gratitude. Each item has significance; each item has a story. Tears and laughter intermingle as we look at and handle each remnant of our loved one's life. We can't keep them all, but we can keep the memories.

After MAID

Geneviève shares how for her, the process of going through her husband's belongings evoked feelings of nostalgia.

Geneviève

The day after my husband died, the kids and I had decided we would go through my husband's stuff and sort it into things to keep, things to gift, things to throw away and things to donate.

For many this would not be something that they would want to do, but for us, it seemed to work.

We went through each drawer and cupboard, talking about every sweater, shirt, and jacket. It brought him back to life in those moments, and we all chose items to keep that made us feel good about him. We shared stories, laughed at how goofy or silly he used to look in certain items and how fond he was of others. We remembered how only he could get away with wearing the short rugby shorts, how retro his jacket made him look, how peculiar some of his tastes were, and how proud he was of his very feminine Stampede shirts.

In his jewelry box, we found items from his father, which led to sharing memories of him as well. He had kept various buttons and pins, a few watch faces, cubes that looked like blank dice, and a few random items. I kept his cologne. It reminded me of him in days when we were young and newly in love. We earmarked his rugby flags for a friend who was also a rugby ref. Some of his things we felt belonged at the cabin.

We spent most of the day together remembering my husband as we sorted through his things. It was sad and good all at the same time. It was very nostalgic. I have occasionally wished we had waited a little longer after he died to do this. Maybe I would have done something with some of his T-shirts or rugby shirts, but then, I am not sure I actually would have gotten around to doing it.

When we had finished, we piled the items to donate into the car and dropped it all off at Goodwill, and then came home and walked the dog together. All in all, it was a very nice day.

How Do You Feel?
How did feelings of nostalgia manifest for you?

CONNECTED

Feeling connected with a loved one after they've died can be a source of great joy. For a few seconds, they are alive again and sharing the present with you. Their old, healthy selves are back, and time stands still. Sometimes, these connections happen in dreams and at other times in response to a certain event that vividly reminds us of our loved one. These moments of connection are precious.

Dave L. describes how he continues to feel connected with his wife Annie since she died.

Dave L.

Annie wanted her burial to take place as soon after her death as possible, so there was a busyness that kept my mind and body occupied for much of the first day after her death. The connection between us that had transcended her death quickly settled into a sense of presence, of sharing the same space, even the same body, not in an intrusive way, but with a sense of something beyond ease. There was and is a sense of rightness about our relationship and a sense of joy. In the first few days that followed, there were moments of grief that lasted ten to fifteen minutes but ended in a moment of connection. Soon, the periods of grief could be measured in minutes or seconds, to be replaced in time with a momentary sadness and then joy as we connected over some experience.

Among the greatest challenges in the first weeks after Annie's death were the cards that I received from her. You'd have to know Annie to understand what I'm talking about. One of Annie's greatest pleasures in life was the writing and sending of cards in elaborately decorated envelopes, a pleasure she indulged in during the last few weeks of her life by creating a stash of cards to be mailed when she was gone.

It was about three days after her death that I received the first one. At first there was anticipation, then grief, then anger at the grief. "Get over it," was the mental response from Annie and eventually, after eight or ten more cards and letters, I did. Although I know the keeper of the cards, neither she nor I ever talked about them. I don't know if there will be more.

It's now 18 months since Annie died and as I reflect on the journey traveled, what comes to mind is the change in our relationship that began when she was accepted into the MAID program. In that moment, there was the experience of release from so much of the baggage we had been carrying. During the weeks before her death, the release continued, supported by the love and compassion we felt for each other: the gift of that last day and our last moments of physical contact.

Each release brought a lightness to the relationship, dissolving the boundaries between life and death and between each other.

How Do You Feel?

Did or do you feel connected to your loved one? Have they 'come back' to you in dreams or through memories? Does this bring you comfort? Write about the times when you felt connected to your loved one following MAID.

Chapter 7

PEACEFUL

For many of us, feeling intense pressure is a normal part of each day leading up to our loved one's MAID. We are frightened and anxious one moment, and frantically busy the next. The last thing we are in those days is peaceful. And then our loved one at last escapes their pain and suffering, and we are free to welcome peace back into our world.

Jane shares how she felt calm and peaceful following the death of her husband.

Jane

I wandered my house alone, sort of floating, unaware of the outside world, as families planned festive visits and elaborate Thanksgiving meals. My husband George had been dead for two days and I remember lying on the bed feeling warm inside and out, calm and ethereal. It was so unlike the feelings I'd had these last years. It seemed impossible that my feelings and his life could have changed so much in the blink of an eye. I realized that a huge weight had been lifted at the exact moment of my husband's death and I felt peaceful.

Later I sat calmly overlooking the lake and breathed deeply the warm breeze. I felt the knots in my stomach loosen. My jaw wasn't tense, and my hands felt relaxed in my lap. I was definitely in a place of peace.

As it was Thanksgiving weekend, I was determined that his death would not darken future Thanksgivings because, in fact, there were many things to be thankful for. I was thankful that this horrible ordeal was over. I was thankful that he had the courage to end his suffering...and mine. I suppose that's where feelings of such deep peace came from...the end of our suffering. As I went to bed that night. I was able to thank George for releasing us from that suffering and giving me peace.

How Do You Feel?

Is peace a feeling that you have experienced in relation to your loved one's medically assisted death?

Chapter 7

WHAT'S YOUR STORY?

Not everyone experiences a MAID death in the same way. Some of us feel a range of emotions all along the way, some of us just get through the experience and then fall apart, and some of us slowly process and feel the effects of the MAID experience for months or years.

Listed below are each of the emotions presented. Take some time to process your own emotions and your reactions to the emotions that the storytellers shared in this chapter.

- Sadness
- Bereft
- Overwhelmed
- Exhausted
- Abandoned
- Empty

- Angry
- Lost
- Nostalgic
- Connected
- Peaceful

How Do You Feel?

Which emotions and stories resonate with you?

Which emotions do not resonate with you?

What emotions did you feel that were not included?

Has anything that you've felt during your journey surprised you?

CHAPTER 8 -

FINDING SUPPORT AFTER MAID

We feel alone, and in this we are connected. — Leo Babauta

After the first months of intense grief have passed and we have become resigned to life without our loved one, we may start to try and return to some routines, or we may start looking for support. While resources to help cope with grief are plentiful, support specific to medically assisted death may not be readily available. MAID is unique in that our loved one chose their end. We knew the date and time and we believed we had time to prepare.

As we face life without our loved one, we may begin to realize that even if we were prepared for their death event, we were not actually prepared for how we were going to feel, or for how we'd return to normal routines and daily life.

Traditional grief counselling may work for some, but it may also miss some of the unique aspects of MAID-related grief. Well-meaning friends often have no idea how to relate to what we've gone through. The desire to reach out and connect with others who have experienced a loved one's MAID, to find others who truly understand and connect with our emotions and experience, is common.

Chapter 8

Our storytellers share how they realized they needed support, and where they looked for help to cope with their loved one's medically assisted death.

CONNECTED

One of the ways we seek support is to connect with others with a similar experience, which in this case, is people who have also been through a loved one's MAID. Sharing our pain and sorrow with people who know first-hand about medically assisted death may provide us with a context for our grief. When we realize that we are not alone, the burden lifts just a little and we are able to carry on.

Cathy and Dave B. share how connecting with others — from friends to people who had first-hand experience of MAID — helped soften the pain of losing their loved ones.

Cathy

I was worn down from a year and a half of caretaking and I was totally overwhelmed. I was afraid of what would happen if I was left alone for long spells. I was worried I'd plunge into some dark abyss and wouldn't know how to get out. I told my friends and family that I needed to be with someone at least once a day. It didn't have to be for long and I didn't care what we did so long as I wasn't sitting alone staring out the window all day.

I was like an octopus, reaching out for help in all directions. This surprised me because one of the things I had always prided myself on was my independence and my ability to take care of my own stuff. It came from being an only child, from going through a divorce, and from having a stiff upper lip philosophy drilled into me from birth. But here I was, asking everyone to help me.

Finding Support After MAID

They responded to what I asked. We met to walk our dogs together, watch TV or just to talk. My best friend of more than 30 years knows me so well that I felt safe pouring my heart out to her. She would listen to my pain, and it felt like some small part of the burden I was carrying passed from my shoulders to hers.

I saw my sons and their spouses several times a week for many months. They both invited me to live with them permanently and their generosity told me I was loved.

My granddaughter and I had become very close when her partner was killed in a tragic accident. She faced the horror and pain of that with a wisdom and maturity well beyond her years and she shared that with me when I needed it most. She talked about how in the early days she always felt like she was falling. When I had the same frightening sensation, I thought back to what she had said and was comforted to know it would pass.

Over time, I joined two support groups for those who had lost a loved one through MAID. I felt validated by these groups and incredibly relieved to know I wasn't the only one experiencing an avalanche of emotions. Although both groups have officially ended, we continue to meet once a week, and we've formed a bond that can only come from shared pain.

When Gary was still alive, the community support services offered us a spiritual counselor. We looked at each other and said why not? Although neither of us was religious, somehow the process of facing Gary's death had made us more receptive to life. They sent Stephanie, a tiny little Buddhist woman, who soothed us and opened our minds. She was supposed to stop coming after Gary died, but she sensed my need and arranged to extend her visits.

They say it takes a village to raise a child. For me, it also took a village to help me with my grief. And following the darkness and pain of that gruelling year and a half while Gary was ill, my village helped me see and experience that there was still love and light in the world.

Dave B.

When Annie died, I was not aware of any supports for me in my grief. Annie and I had gone to a cancer support agency, and they were helpful for her in some ways, but my principal feeling was that they and I were on the same team helping to support Annie. They did not offer any kind of survivor support after she died.

While I don't have any definite memories of the early months after Annie's death, I did feel early on that I wanted to become involved with the medically assisted dying movement. My first attempt was after I read an opinion piece in the *New York Times*, written by a woman whose best friend had died by suicide. She decided to get involved with Dying with Dignity Canada as a volunteer witness for MAID applications. I thought immediately that I could do that too.

While checking out DWDC's Facebook page I learned about the MAID Family Support Society. I contacted the founder and enrolled as a volunteer peer-to-peer support person. Doing this work makes me feel closer to Annie. It reminds me that I am in the same kind of place as the person I'm listening to.

Sometimes listening to the stories of others brings tears to my eyes, and it feels so good to grieve their loss along with my own. Being in grief with someone else is a wonderful way of sharing and connecting. In offering support to others, I've found the greatest support and connection to Annie.

Whenever someone asks about Annie's death, I always answer briefly, but then focus more on Annie's life—her passions, what brought her joy, her close friends, and best of all, her love for me.

How Do You Feel?
Did you want to connect with others who had experienced MAID? What motivated you to seek support and how did connecting with others help you?

UNDERSTOOD

In many communities, MAID is relatively uncommon and can be quite stigmatized, which can leave us feeling isolated and alone in our grief. One of the greatest gifts we can receive is to connect with someone who understands what we are going through and who can empathize and listen.

Daimhin shares how feeling understood by her best friend helped support her following her father's MAID death.

Daimhin

A couple of days after my dad died, my best friend Max came over. We normally would have hung out in the kitchen, sitting in the heart of my loud household while my family laughed and talked together. But when she arrived, the house was silent. We went downstairs to my bedroom, got under my heavy duvet, and just looked at each other. Within minutes and without saying anything much, we were both crying. I could see the sympathy on her face, but also a look of understanding. Her dad was also sick, and we had been supporting each other for the past year. I didn't need to say anything; she just understood. Her dad was sick, and she was terrified of losing him. It wasn't a stretch for her to imagine what I was feeling that day during my first week without a father. I didn't have to explain anything to her. We stayed in bed for a while, talking, crying, and we shared a few laughs as well. As we laid there, I felt a glimmer of hope growing in my dark and empty body. I could feel that with a support system like this, I could continue to put one foot in front of the other and get through the darkest stages of grief. Having Max, that person who could support me from a place of understanding was, and still is, invaluable.

Eleven months later, Max's dad chose MAID as well. I was able to support her in the ways she supported me, even better sometimes, because I just knew. There were so many thoughts, feelings and emotions that came up while each of us processed the loss of our fathers, but the bond of our shared experience made it easier. I never felt crazy or misunderstood. There was always Max there to just 'get it' and understand how I was feeling. Even now, three years later, she is still the first person I call if I have a 'bad Dad day.' We talk, laugh and cry together and it has made all the difference in my journey with losing my dad. It feels horrible to say it, but I am so grateful that we both had this shared experience so we could lean on and support each other.

How Do You Feel?
Who do you feel most understands your MAID experience?

LOVE

Love is a word that comes up frequently among our storytellers. Respecting the wishes of a loved one who has chosen MAID is an incredible act of love that resonates long after the loved one has passed. How do we keep this love alive? One way is to reach out to close friends and family to both offer and ask for support.

Dave L. describes how telling others about the love he and his wife Annie shared continues to support him. Bobbie shares how the support she received from her friend Sally and women in a

Finding Support After MAID

Parkinson's support group helped her get through the first months of intense grief following the death of her husband.

Dave L.

Good friends are all the support needed on this journey. Annie and I were best friends; we had a relationship filled with generosity, love, compassion and joy. There were moments when one of us would forget, but more often than not, the other would remember and bring us back on track.

Early in our relationship Annie insisted we sit down weekly and spend time in conversation, answering three questions: "Tell me something you like about me, tell me something you think we agree on and tell me something you think I should know about yourself." Nothing in our relationship stayed hidden for very long. The opportunity to be listened to, without interruption by someone who is fully present to what is being spoken and the opportunity to reach deep into oneself and speak what is true in the moment is the power that supports a beautiful friendship.

Annie was often labeled the sick person and I the caregiver. These were not useful labels, and it often took effort not to fall into the trap of using them ourselves. There is a mutuality in a caring relationship, in which each cares for the other. Annie understood this and it's who she was. She was a caregiver in the true meaning of the word. When we met, I was an engineer, a guy who fixed things. For Annie, I was somebody in need of care. To Annie, I will always be a work in progress, she took care of me in ways that often began with my resistance and were only later appreciated for the life changing effects they had. Yoga, meditation, encouraging interests, friendships, projects, even if it meant time away from being together. It is her caring and the caring of other good friends that supports me now.

During the last few weeks of her life, we spent a lot of time talking about what I would do after she died. We talked about how I

217

could share with others the powerful experiences we had during those last two months of her life. It is in that caring for and sharing with others that I find the support I need.

It's not easy relinquishing our starring role in the movie of life, but it's from a seat in the audience, in the company of a good friend that we will find wisdom and joy.

Bobbie

For some unknown reason, I joined the Parkinson's support group just two weeks after Bob died. It was WAY too early. My grief was so raw that I literally wept for the entire 90 minutes. Two weeks later, I managed to stop weeping at 45 minutes and joked to the group about how much better I was doing.

The group was life saving in so many ways. Our grief counsellor, who had been doing this for many years, offered so much honest information and hope for the future. She was very practical about what grief was doing to my body and mind and made me feel much better about the fact that I couldn't empty the dishwasher in less than three days.

I feel blessed to have this wonderful group of women who started my grief walk with me. Not all of them were people whom I saw regularly, but they made sure I never walked alone. It was wonderful to have them share their lives as well, which helped me navigate my own complete and utter despair. Having a variety of different people to share this daunting journey with made it so much easier for me. I never felt that I was putting too much pressure on any one person, and I loved the feeling of women helping women.

But the strongest support came from my friend Sally. She was there every single day in some way. She was incredibly busy at the time, but still called, walked, and met me for endless cups of

London Fog. She kept me moving forward when honestly, I had no interest in tomorrow.

As I look back, I see that it took a whole village to keep me going, daily emojis and happy baby photos from my almost children, special cocktails from my neighbour, endless food and treats, so many texts and emails and phone calls.

They all gave of their time and heart to help me move forward with such tiny, tiny steps.

How Do You Feel?

How can you transform your love for the person who chose MAID so that it supports you as you go forward into your life without them? Take some time to write about the love you had for your person.

LONELY

Loneliness can be a real challenge following the death of a loved one. If you've been used to having someone in your life, how do you cope when they are no longer with you? And if you don't know anyone who has supported a loved one through MAID, you may feel additionally isolated. You may not know who to talk with who will be able to understand your experience.

Brittney shares how her mother's death left her longing to connect with someone who understood her pain. For Elizabeth, the loneliness she felt after losing first her mother and then her father to MAID was overwhelming. Carol shares how she felt isolated and alone following the passing of her mother.

Chapter 8

Brittney

The days quickly turned into weeks following my mom's passing. After the funeral, I knew that it was time to get groceries, check the mail, put gas in the car and go back to work, but I wasn't ready, I was still numb. *Why get groceries when I never felt hungry? Why get gas when I didn't feel like going anywhere?* I have never felt so isolated in my life. I could be in a room packed with people, but I still felt like I was the only one there.

Not long before my mom died, she made a point to strongly encourage my family to seek some sort of counselling after her death. I had mixed feelings about whether it would help me or not.

As the weeks turned into months, I noticed that going out in public still seemed like a chore, and I really didn't care about much of anything. My mom was dead; I couldn't see a way back to living 'normally' again. I felt bitter and jealous when I would scroll through social media. I could not stand the smiling, happy faces.

How can they be so happy? Don't they know my world has literally stopped? Screw those people!

I was a hot mess. I was emotional, irritable and barely eating or sleeping. I decided it was time for me to start grief counselling. I still had mixed feelings, unsure if it would actually help me or not.

Will it make me feel less lonely and isolated? Will they think I'm crazy?

My mom was right, I did need professional support. I started weekly sessions right away. It felt good to talk, vent, and cry. It was also very reassuring to be told that the things I was feeling and thinking were normal, and that I was not crazy. My counsellor had also lost someone close to her using MAID, so I quickly connected with her. The isolated feeling didn't feel as heavy or intense anymore.

Slowly but surely, I started eating again and sleeping more, and I decided to go back to work. My mom used to say, "one day at a time." So that's what I did. I would still wake up and fall asleep feeling isolated and heartbroken, but I got through the days as best I could, putting on my fake smile, keeping busy, and allowing myself the occasional break down in my shower. I can still hear my mom's voice in my head encouraging me. I just keep taking things one day at a time, like my mom always did. Some days are total shit shows, BUT some are pretty damn good!

Elizabeth

Loneliness was overwhelming, not perhaps in the true sense of the word as I had my loved ones around me, but I felt alone in the wilderness with my feelings. I felt like I was taking a journey, perhaps like a road trip where you don't always know what stops you will make or what the destination looks like.

When Mom had MAID in 2016, there weren't any support groups or peer support people that I could talk to about the uniqueness of the death situation. My siblings and my dad could relate to the uniqueness of MAID, but they were going through their own process, having lost Mom as well.

I learned quickly that I had to be very selective about who I tried to discuss this with outside of my direct family. Some of the people around me were quick to judge or looked down on me for my mother's choice. Others told me they thought she had made a selfish choice. I was struggling to breathe and keep my head above water, feeling like waves were washing over me relentlessly, never knowing which way to turn to find comfort or relief.

Chapter 8

When Dad had MAID in 2021, I didn't feel like I was gasping for air the way I had five years earlier, but I certainly felt adrift in some ocean somewhere. Again, my siblings and our families were grieving my dad, but we were each on our own journey. I felt very lonely at times because I didn't want to burden the people around me.

As hard as I tried, I couldn't reach land, and when I thought I was actually back on solid ground again, I was completely exhausted, but I still needed to watch for the undercurrents.

Carol

For months after my mom passed, I felt like I was living in a fog. I have never sought counseling before and now looking back, I wish I had. I thought I needed to power through on my own because 'MAID is different than other deaths.' I didn't understand why I was so grief-stricken because, after all, Mom had chosen her path. Also, she had been miserable, so wasn't it selfish to wish her back? I should have been relieved that she was in a better place, but instead I just felt completely alone. Some days, I could barely get off the couch. I felt frozen and numb, unable to just be sad, but also not able or willing to talk about it.

After several months, I finally decided to seek out people who may have some experience with MAID. A quick Google search led me to an online support group. I only attended one session, but that one time was tremendously helpful to me. Finally, I realized that I was not alone.

How Do You Feel?

Write about how feelings of loneliness affected your desire and ability to seek support. If your loved one is considering MAID, how and where do you think you will find support after they die?

INFERIOR

Grief can sometimes be seen as having different hierarchies and different levels of intensity. The grief felt following an unexpected death, like that of a child, might be considered much worse than the grief felt after an expected or planned death, like the passing of an aged parent. But that, of course, is not true. Grief is grief. When we love someone, no matter what the relationship — child, spouse, parent, friend, and so on — we will feel grief when they die. We shouldn't need to justify ourselves or feel like our grief is somehow 'less than' compared to others.

Shannon shares how her grief at losing her friend felt inferior to the grief of others who lost family members, which led her to seek support and validation.

Shannon

After Wendy died, I was conflicted by the intensity of my emotions and the complexity of understanding my relationship to her. Wendy wasn't my mother or sister or spouse. The label on our relationship didn't seem to allow me, or others, to accept my profound grief. I found it challenging to find support that didn't place me into the category of 'just a friend.' I may have even plopped myself into that category based on my own interpretation of the societal construct of what friendship is. Apparently, I wasn't 'close enough' to grieve Wendy.

I attended an online group session for a few weeks with other people who had experienced MAID losses of parents, grandparents, siblings, and spouses. No one ever said I was 'just a friend' out loud, but I couldn't help but feel completely out of place. It was difficult to share my experience because I felt my grief was not as significant or valid. I felt inferior to those who had sustained losses of family members. There doesn't seem to be a place for the 'just friends' to find community in their grief, although I'm fairly certain there are many more grieving friends like me out there.

I remember one of the only places where I felt my grief was allowed to exist was in my counselor's office. I was sitting in the black leather chair, legs crossed, flat-faced and exhausted. The pandemic had been daunting and devastating to work through, and I was a burnt-out wreck before Wendy passed.

I angrily ranted and rambled on about work at my appointment with Lisa, my counselor. My rant fizzled out and a short silence ensued. Then Lisa asked about Wendy. Immediately, tears burned in my eyes and I hid my face in my hands. She continued, "It's painful...to lose someone you love." I knew I loved Wendy; I'd even told her many times. But for some reason, hearing someone else acknowledge my pain and my grief and my love for my friend allowed me to feel it. Every muscle in my body tensed uncontrollably as I violently wept.

How Do You Feel?

Has your grief felt inferior or unjustified compared to others in your MAID experience?

FRUSTRATED

You may discover that you are not able to find the support you need following your loved one's MAID. Even if you find support, you may not get what you need or find a person whose story you can relate to. This situation can lead to feelings of frustration and loneliness.

Finding Support After MAID

Andrée shares how frustrated she felt when she couldn't find someone who could relate to her experience as a parent who lost a child to MAID.

Andrée

I've been looking for support for six years. It would be nice to have someone to talk to who could relate to what I am going through, what I've been through. The groups I have found specific to child loss were full of people who had lost a young child, but my daughter was an adult when she died, so I didn't feel like I belonged there.

Shortly after Kim died, I found a support group for loved ones of people who chose MAID, but I still didn't find anyone I could relate to. No one there had lost a child. They had all lost either a parent or a spouse. I've also lost my parents and my husband, but losing my child was, and still is, different. It is so frustrating that there is no support out there for parents like me. I just want to talk to someone who understands my loss, and my sadness at all the things Kim will never experience. Only another parent can recognize the joy and pain that comes with talking about the child you lost. It would be comforting to be able to talk to someone who gets it, instead of the empathy or pity I am used to receiving when I tell people that I've lost a child.

I'd like to know how other parents respond when asked how many children they have. Is it okay to talk about the child we lost or only the ones who are living? Do they talk openly about MAID? How do people react? I feel my daughter was so brave to choose MAID, and it frustrates me that I can't find a community that can share in my grieving process.

SADNESS

Sadness takes many forms and may last far longer than we think it 'should.' It takes its toll both physically and emotionally, leaving us feeling wrung out and lethargic. But there is no timeline to sadness — it lasts for as long as it needs to, and truly never goes away.

Jane shares her realization of the depths of her sadness, which led her to seek support following the death of her husband.

Jane

About a year after my husband's death, two other clergy persons and I ran a grief support group. I felt that I had 'moved on' far enough from his death to be part of the leadership. After the second weekly session, I felt incredibly sad, and then in week three, I totally forgot about the group and didn't show up to the meeting. I was mortified that I could do such a thing, but soon realized that I was subconsciously avoiding my own buried grief. I had not 'moved on' from my husband's death as much as I'd thought.

When you start unpacking the feeling of sadness, it's amazing the other feelings you find lurking in the shadows. For me, sadness was not a welcome feeling. It made me tearful at the drop of a hat and as a result I felt very vulnerable. The sadness was like a dark cloud that I would try to get out from under but couldn't shake it. I could fake being happy for a bit, but any mention of other people's grief or sadness would make me teary. When these emotional episodes happened, I would retreat, physically so that others wouldn't see my upset, and emotionally into a dark hole that left me tired and immobilized. My feet felt like lead, and the only thing I could do was sit.

I chose a trusted colleague to open up to who allowed me to be quiet until I was able to express myself. This sadness made me think I was inadequate in some way, wondering how I could be strong for others if I was tearful all the time? Being 'brave' was my way of abandoning my grief and not caring enough for my own emotional well being. I realized that sadness was choking me and holding me back from finding out who I was to become in this next chapter of my life.

How Do You Feel?

How did your sadness present itself after your loved one's medically assisted death?

THANKFUL

At first, seeking out support may feel impossible. How can anyone really understand what you are going through? But over time, the need for connection may lead you to find a counselor, a peer support group, or some other form of help that makes you feel seen and heard. Connecting in this way is a reminder that you are not alone and can provide tremendous relief and feelings of gratitude.

Emily shares how thankful she felt once she connected with support groups to help her cope with the loss of her wife.

Chapter 8

Emily

I never thought in my wildest dreams I would find someone I would be able to love, let alone it being another woman. Veronica was my soul mate, my best friend, my everything. I am so grateful for the life she and I made together. I know she felt the same and wanted to make sure I was taken care of after she was no longer here because she helped me find a counselor months before she died. Knowing she was thinking of me, even in her toughest days, reminds me how much she loved me.

Life without Veronica hit me like a ton of bricks. I was depressed for months, barely able to work, eat or even sleep. I had friends who would text or call, which made a difference in getting me through the first few months, but I found it wasn't enough. I was so sad, lonely and lost. It got so bad that I didn't want to be here anymore. A friend was persistent and checked on me every day and my brothers and father checked on me too. I wanted more for myself, but I didn't know where to find people who would understand how I was feeling.

I found a number of grief support groups online that allowed me to share space and stories with others who had the same type of loss as me. I didn't feel so alone knowing there were people I could talk to who had shared experiences like mine. Before I knew it, I was a part of four different support groups. Having a place for my grief to be witnessed made me feel seen, understood, and even loved. There was no judgment from anyone, and it felt great. I stopped wanting to die and began to imagine living in this world without Veronica. I'm so grateful to have found these support groups and the people in them. They saved my life.

I would recommend going out and searching for grief support groups that may help you.

How Do You Feel?

Did you find support that was helpful after your loved one's death? Was it MAID-specific support? How did finding support make you feel?

LOST

Sometimes the death of a loved one combined with the other responsibilities of life lead us to feeling completely and utterly lost. Seeking out support can feel like an additional chore that we just can't handle and can lead us to choose coping mechanisms that are not healthy.

Nikki shares about her battle with the bottle, and her attempt to numb how lost she felt.

Nikki

The truth is that I didn't seek support from groups or organizations affiliated with MAID. Maybe I would have if I had known they existed, but that was never really my style. I didn't join mommy groups when I had my babies, and I sure as shit wasn't feeling the desire to join a 'my dad chose to have MAID' group.

I had my therapist and my husband and friends to lean on. I also leaned on several bottles of rum. And vodka. Really, anything that would numb the horrendous variety of emotions that consumed me from the moment I woke up and almost choked on the feeling of remembering my dad was dead until I fell into a numb slumber. I had been through hell, and I was completely overwhelmed. I was lost. I was just trying to keep my head above water and do all the things society expected of me, to just jump back in and do life well.

Chapter 8

I was experiencing levels of anxiety and depression I had never felt in my 39-year life. Things felt very dark. Like a heavy cloud hanging around me, constantly reminding me of how crappy things were. I was sad about my dad. I was mad at my nuclear family, and I was so very burnt out and lost. I felt alone, and alcohol became my dear friend for a while. I remember telling my husband, "Don't worry. I am fully aware of what I am doing. Right now, I need to just do this to survive". It wasn't pretty. My father was an alcoholic. And for the first time in my life, I dipped my toe into experiencing what it felt like to need something to really survive the day.

So, did it help? A little. It helped me get through the evenings without losing my cool with my kids. But it also added a new layer of guilt and fear. I felt guilty that I couldn't hack it without numbing myself in a bottle, and for not being a present mother. I felt like an awful mother. I feared I wouldn't be able to stop.

Approximately nine months passed. Then one day, I looked at a bottle that was three-quarters empty after only two days and it literally shocked me back to needing to find sobriety. I was stunned that I had consumed so much alcohol on my own. It reminded me of a time I had watched my dad examine a bottle of scotch he was working on, the way I was looking at this one, and that was it for me.

I don't feel particularly proud to share this low point of mine, but I am proud I found a different path for my grief than my father did.

How Do You Feel?
Can you relate to feeling lost after your experience with MAID? How did you realize that you needed support?

RESENTFUL

After a loved one dies, life for many people is never the same again and it feels unfair that this has happened to you. Acceptance is not easy, especially when people around you are not hurting the way you are. Finding support can be hard, impossible even, when you resent the people who are trying to help you.

Cynthia shares how she felt resentful towards anyone who wasn't a young widow after her husband died.

Cynthia

The day my husband died was a day that marked me and changed me for forever. From this point on, everything would be referred to as before he died, and after he died. I expected to feel sad, scared, lost and even lonely, but I didn't expect to feel so alienated and misunderstood. I wasn't prepared for the additional loss of friends and supporters who disappeared from our lives. I felt very resentful towards the people who misunderstood us, hurt less than we did, and then left us.

When my husband died, I was suddenly a single mom of two young kids, trying to navigate our oceans of grief as well as the daily details of life. I started to notice the abundance of superficial things in life that I just didn't have time for. I lost my patience for small talk and other people's trivial problems. I had no desire to participate in or deal with anything that wasn't crucial to my children's well being.

I found it hard to connect with the people whose lives seemed to be ticking along with less trauma or struggle than ours. I didn't want to sugar coat my words or dig deep to offer empathy or sympathy to others for situations that seemed bad for them but felt enviable to me. I resented their seemingly easy woes. I grew irritated at the need to explain my actions and inactions, and my grief to my family and friends. The contradictory messaging that as a mother of bereft children I should both 'put the kids first' and 'take care of myself, because I can't pour from an empty cup' was infuriating.

The day my husband died, people who had been my closest friends and confidants suddenly had nothing important in common with me. My married friends were still married, but I was single. My divorced friends shared custody of their children, but I was a full-time guardian. My friends' sick spouses were still alive, and I was planning a funeral. My friends' children still had fathers, while mine did not. My single friends were searching for the love of their lives, and I was missing mine. I hated them for what they had not lost.

I'd joined a club, widowhood, that I hadn't applied to be part of, and no one else that I knew or liked was a member yet. And the truth was that I wasn't liking them much anymore because they were still in the old, happily married club that I had never wanted to leave. I resented their ability to keep living the life that I was missing.

My resentment didn't start to fade until I met other members of this dreaded club who could personally relate to my day-to-day struggles. I found my refuge amongst other young, widowed mothers who shared my grief and had lived a similar trauma.

How Do You Feel?

What role did resentment play in your experience? Who did you feel resentful towards?

WHAT'S YOUR STORY?

Finding support can be a natural process, or it can require effort. Sometimes the support that is available before a MAID loss is not as helpful as the support we need afterwards. Some of us want support and some of us don't, and some of us don't realize that we need support. A lot of feelings present themselves as we work through our grief and discover what kind of support we have, want, and need.

Listed below are each of the emotions presented as our storytellers found support.

- Connected
- Understood
- Love
- Lonely
- Inferior

- Sadness
- Frustrated
- Thankful
- Lost
- Resentful

How Do You Feel?

Which emotions and stories resonate with you?

Which emotions do not resonate with you?

What emotions did you feel that were not included?

Has anything that you've felt during your journey surprised you?

CHAPTER 9 -

MOVING FORWARD

Being deeply loved by someone gives you strength,
while loving someone deeply gives you courage. -
Lao Tzu

Life goes on after the death of our loved one, even if some days we may wish everything would just stop and time would turn backwards to when we still had them in our lives. But eventually, we do find ways to move forward in life. The sadness and the ache in our hearts never goes away, but it softens over time as we learn to navigate our new reality.

One way to move forward is to find a way to 'give back.' *The Many Faces of MAID* provided our storytellers with an opportunity to share their experience with others. Working on the book also provided each of us with an opportunity to process our emotions, connect with one another, and it gave us some perspective on how far we have each come since MAID touched our lives.

But working on this book was not the only way in which our storytellers moved forward. In this final chapter of *The Many Faces of MAID*, discover the emotions that each of us are experiencing as we propel ourselves into the future.

PROUD

Learning to stand on your own two feet without the support of your loved one can be daunting, particularly if you've spent the better part of your life with them. Their influence is everywhere and your memories of them are constant and overwhelming. Moving forward feels impossible, and yet when you do, you may feel a tremendous sense of pride and accomplishment.

Cathy and Emily share how they felt proud of themselves when they were able to go on with their lives following the deaths of their spouses.

Cathy

I'm proud of what I've accomplished in the 15 months since Gary died. I've always had a strong sense of what's right for me, and fortunately that kicked in as I navigated the painful and challenging business of living life alone.

About five months after Gary died, I sat staring out the window one winter day and realized I had to do what all the books tell you not to do in the first year — I had to move. Not only did I feel isolated and alone, but his presence was everywhere. If I fell asleep on the couch watching TV, I expected him to be sitting in his Lazy Boy across from me when I opened my eyes. If the dog cuddled up to me during the night, I'd wake thinking it was him. God knows I didn't want to forget Gary, but I had to find a way to control my experience without constantly being ambushed by memories.

I started looking for an apartment with only a vague notion of what would feel like home. I surprised myself when I settled on an apartment on the 10th floor of a high-rise. I love that it's directly across from a recreation centre where I take yoga and fitness and steps away from a park where I walk my dog. I probably say hello to 20 people every day and I've made some good friends. I'm proud of myself for listening to my intuition and making such a huge, positive change.

A month after I moved, I found the courage to go to the American Consulate in Toronto and renounce my US citizenship. This was something I had been wanting to do for years but it scared me. I've always been a good girl — a rule follower. Renouncing my citizenship felt like the height of rebellion. But I didn't let my fear stop me and I'm proud of myself for finally following through and getting it done.

Shortly after, I swallowed my pride and bought hearing aids, something Gary had been encouraging me to do for years as he became increasingly tired of telling me what the guy on TV said. It's a relief to be able to take part in conversations again and to stop nodding my head to cover the fact that I hadn't heard what was being said.

That long year and a half of caregiving with its inevitable end was so stressful and immersive that I had pretty well lost my sense of self. Now, I once again feel like I have a future and the will and ability to shape my own life. Sure, there are still times when a dark fog comes over me and I feel sad and alone, but I'm doing what I wasn't sure I'd be able to do. I'm navigating life on my own.

Emily

I'm not going to lie, moving forward was very hard for me. I don't think that I did anything but survive in the first year after Veronica died. I cried a lot, stayed home, and didn't want to face the world without her. The pandemic added an extra layer to my pain because I couldn't have my family and friends sitting with me, giving me hugs and words of encouragement.

My counselor helped me realize that there is no right or wrong way to grieve. He was gentle with me, supporting me, encouraging me, praising me and most of all, he was always there for me. My biggest and scariest fear after Veronica died was how I was going to move forward without her encouragement, love, support, and wisdom. I was scared. When Vee died, my world turned dark for the first year or so. Looking back, I can see how much progress I've made.

I gained the strength to reach out for support. I joined several support groups. I was so scared to put myself out there and participate, but it was the best thing that I could have done. Being a part of a grief and loss group allowed me to share my story…our love story. At the end of one group, some participants thanked me for being so open and honest and said I had helped them in their healing journey. It brought joy to me to know that I was helping someone by talking about my losses.

I know that my Vee and my momma are proud of me for picking myself up off the ground and getting back up and trying to be the compassionate person I once was, only better. I am also very proud of myself for being brave enough to put my love story out to the world. Much love and light to everyone who has lost an important person who has walked this earth.

How Do You Feel?
As you move forward after your MAID experience, what makes you feel proud?

SADNESS

Although your sadness might shift and soften, it will never go away. Sadness settles into your bones and becomes an integral part of your very existence. You likely carry your loved one in

Chapter 9

your heart as a persistent ache that every so often explodes into pain as acute as the pain you felt the day you watched them die.

As you keep moving forward on your journey without your loved one, this sadness can sometimes take you by surprise at the most unexpected times. You never know when this will happen, but you soon come to realize that it's all part of the process.

Daimhin shares the sadness that gripped her when she was reminded of activities she'd enjoyed with her dad, and Andrée shares the sadness she knows will be with her forever.

Daimhin

My boyfriend, Ryan, and I had just finished watching *Doctor Strange and the Multiverse of Madness*. A few years before he died, my dad and I watched every Marvel movie to prepare for *Infinity War* and saw all the Marvel movies in the theatres together since then.

As I walked out of the theatre, I realized this was the fifth Marvel movie since dad died that I had to see without him. With that realization, it felt like someone had punched me in the stomach. My mind spiralled as I wondered just how many Marvel movies he will miss in my lifetime. How many seasons of our favourite show, *Big Mouth*, he won't sit beside me to watch? How many life milestones of mine he won't be there for?

He didn't see me graduate university or start my first job. He didn't get to see me fall in love or move across the country to live with my partner. He will never walk me down the aisle at my wedding and he won't meet the kids I hope to have. My face flushed as all of these thoughts came flying at me. I could feel the tears pricking my eyes, so I rushed outside to avoid all the people in the theatre. Before Ryan could even ask what was wrong, my tears were streaming down my face and I was gasping for air, sobbing into his chest.

In that moment, the agony of losing my dad was as fresh as it was the day he died. I felt pain radiating through my body and was convinced that I could cry forever. It seemed like that pain and those tears would continue until I physically couldn't cry anymore and then my tear ducts would just fill back up, and I would continue to cry and cry until the end of time. My sorrow was infinite and all encompassing, just like it was the last time it visited me.

My moments of sadness have become less frequent over the years, but the pain is just as fresh and real as it always has been. It may rest below the surface, but its severity has not dissipated.

Andrée

It has been six years since my adult daughter chose MAID. I still miss her everyday. I will always miss her. I can't shake the sadness I feel each time something special happens in our life and Kim is not part of it. It creeps up on me, starting as a tickle in the back of my throat, and then warm tears flood my eyes and I have to swallow hard to keep from bursting into tears.

Her sister got married last year. Kim would have been so happy to see her walk down the aisle. I tried to include Kim in the ceremony by adding a special charm to her sister's bouquet, but it didn't feel like enough. I felt so happy being at my daughter's wedding, but there was still a part of my heart that was acutely aware that Kim was missing. She never got to meet her sister's wife.

Although I hate public speaking, I gave the Maid of Honor speech that Kim left for me to read at her sister's wedding reception. It was so hard. I held back tears knowing Kim should have been there to give the speech herself.

Her sister and I talk about Kim often— her reaction to things like COVID, what a wonderful aunt she would have been to my seven-month-old grandson— and each conversation is tinged with sadness. It's like even the happiest of moments will never be truly and fully happy because part of me is gone. Some days I can laugh knowing she would have had strong opinions on so many things. Most times though, I hold back my tears because she isn't here. She should be enjoying life with us and the fact that she isn't causes a sadness that I will never overcome.

How Do You Feel?
When do you feel most sad? What triggers your sadness?

INCOMPLETE

There is no timetable for grief. It takes as long as it takes to ride the waves. You may expect them to get smaller over time, but that's not always the case. Some days, the waves are ripples, and other days, they grow into tsunamis. These waves may be accompanied by a restlessness, a feeling of being unfinished or incomplete. You know you are missing your loved one, but you may also feel like you haven't yet processed your grief. Something's missing, and you may not be able to figure out what.

Carol shares how almost two years after her mom's MAID, she is still plagued by feelings of incompleteness, as if there's something more she needs to do to grieve fully.

Carol

I still feel like I haven't fully processed my grief following my mother's MAID. Multiple times a day, a stab of sadness catches in my throat and scrunches my face. I've never really cried like so many people describe, and I desperately wish I could. I feel like

I'm waiting for the storm to hit me, and hope that one day it will so I can finally feel released.

On the surface, I'm doing well. I live a full life doing work I love, and I have a wonderful husband and daughter to support me. Collaborating with Cynthia to put together *The Many Faces of MAID* has been a rewarding way to give back, and I'm very grateful for the experience. I've learned so much about processing my grief and found solace knowing that our book may help others.

But I'm not done with the grief yet — not by a long shot. I wait every day for the big release, the full-on crying jag that will finally drain the grief out of me. But I also know that might not happen. And even if it does, I will continue carrying my sadness close to my heart and missing my mom every day. I'm not sorry she made the choice she did, but I never anticipated how long I would need to 'get over it.' But then, on balance, I don't ever want to get over her.

How Do You Feel?
Has your experience with MAID left you with feelings of being incomplete?

PEACEFUL

Finding peace after the passing of your loved one comes slowly, if at all, and is often accompanied by feelings of gratitude. You learn over time to be thankful that your loved one is no longer suffering and that you have your memories. You may start being able to smile and laugh again, knowing your loved one wouldn't want you to be miserable.

Chapter 9

Brittney shares how she eventually found peace following her mother's MAID.

Brittney

My life was forever changed when my mom died. There is a part of me that is missing now, and I know it will never heal. I found my smile and my laugh when I began using the tools I had acquired in counselling and felt myself feeling less bitter and alone. My smile isn't as big as it once was, my laugh is not as loud, and my light doesn't shine quite as brightly.

I have learned that it's okay to be sad and pissed off. It's okay to get in my car, drive to a random spot and cry my eyes out. It's also okay to laugh. I felt so awful laughing for the first time after my mom died. It felt so taboo, like if I was laughing and having a good time, I wasn't missing her enough or had forgotten that she'd died.

I also learned to focus on the things I was thankful for, starting with the fact that my mom was no longer suffering. Cancer was no longer living inside her — she was free! I am thankful that she is now back to her 'normal self' — beautiful, healthy and eating that big, juicy hamburger she longed for while she was sick. I feel incredibly fortunate that we were able to say goodbye and give her all our love, hugs and 'I love yous.'

Yes, her getting sick was not fair, and I am still angry and jealous of the women my age who have their mothers in their lives. My mom will not be with me when I have kids or get married and that really sucks. I cry when I think about wedding dress shopping in the future, and that she won't be there. I cry when I think about when I have my first kid and have no idea what the hell I'm doing. I cry when all I want to do is text her to see if she wants to go into town shopping together, just for something to do.

I am thankful for MAID and that my mom was able to die on her own terms. I am happy that her transition was everything that she wanted. She didn't let cancer take her. 'Enough was enough.' And I'm so damn proud of my strong as hell, wonder-woman mother. I miss her every single day and always will.

Someone once told me that grieving is like the waves on the beach. Some days, the waves are rough and wild, a complete shit show where you lose control, and some days are calm and quiet. I continue to hear my mom's voice in my head encouraging me to 'take one day at a time.' I ride the rough waves when they come and let them wash over me, and I embrace the calm days when there are no waves at all.

How Do You Feel?
What does peace feel like for you? When do you feel peaceful?

PURPOSEFUL

Finding purpose after your loved one's MAID can be challenging, but ultimately worthwhile. When you have a purpose, you may feel more equipped to make sense of your grief. Often this purpose takes the form of helping others cope with what you have already had to deal with, in our case, MAID. The *Many Faces of MAID* was borne out of our desire to 'give back,' to fill a void that we had all experienced.

Elizabeth shares how she found purpose following the MAID of both her father and her mother when she began volunteering to help others along their MAID journey.

Chapter 9

Elizabeth

It took me a long time after my mother had MAID to even consider being able to do something that would help other people. I was too busy with my own grief. It was about six months after my dad had MAID, that I felt an overwhelming desire to do something with my lived experience. I wanted to 'pay it forward.'

In early 2022, I came across a group online that was providing peer support to people supporting a loved one who was about to have or had already had MAID. They were looking for volunteers. I jumped at the opportunity to be able to talk to people who were going through a journey like I had been through. Even though every situation, person and family dynamics are different, I really wanted to use my experience to help support others in any way that I could.

Volunteering with MAID Family Support Society has been so rewarding. It makes me happy knowing that I have made a difference every time I speak with someone during perhaps one of the most challenging of life's experiences. There are so many layers to MAID, and I wished that there had been a group like this back in 2016 when I really needed it.

As an added benefit I have met some truly amazing and inspiring people. They remind me that we are never truly alone and help me in my own healing process. In working to support others, I've found a community of loss and the support that I was lacking.

Being a part of this book has been an absolute honour and I am so grateful to share my story.

How Do You Feel?
Have you discovered a sense of purpose as a result of your experience with MAID?

INSPIRED

Over time, you may find that the experience of supporting your loved one through MAID has provided you with unexpected gifts in the form of a greater understanding of, and empathy for, the suffering of others in similar situations. You may feel inspired to become better a version of yourself.

Shannon shares how she felt inspired to get involved in helping others after experiencing the pain of losing her friend Wendy.

Shannon

In the year following Wendy's death, I was able to realize (surrender to) my grief, acknowledge its intensity and adapt to living with its ebbs and flows. I let my love for my friend pour out of me in streams of tears as often as I needed to. My grief hasn't left me, but I have found it steals the breath from my chest less frequently.

I'm inspired to get involved, whether it's sharing my experience through this writing or advocating for my own patients with an evolved understanding for what dying is and what it can look like. I'm also inspired to live for right now. Losing Wendy has allowed me to experience life more authentically. I am far more vulnerable and softer than I was before, and my life is much fuller for it. This is a gift I don't really have words for, nor did I expect.

How Do You Feel?
Did your experience with MAID inspire you? In what way?

Chapter 9

SELF-AWARE

Grief is a harsh and yet necessary teacher. When you open yourself to it and accept that you must embrace and process it, you become more aware of who you are and what you need. You may also become more open to change and growth. While the sadness and the fear will still be with you, you may use your new self-awareness to help you seek new experiences and go forward in life without your loved one.

Bobbie shares how she has become more self-aware following her husband's MAID.

Bobbie

My life has changed so much that I sometimes find it hard to know if I have actually moved forward, or just sideways. The grief still hits me so hard that it takes my breath away. I rarely have a day that I don't cry or at least shed a few tears. The memories seem endless and exhausting. But now when I look at photos that come up daily on my iPad, I can smile and remember the good times. I am so thankful that I was the one taking photos because I have a lot, and of course they were all happy times.

I am often paralyzed with fear of facing another challenge alone, but somehow, I find a way to at least try. I was a caregiver for 23 years and did so much, but the difference is huge. I don't have my cheerleader supporting me anymore. Bob called me his Warrior Wife, and somehow Warrior Widow does not have the same cachet.

But thanks to the social worker in my Parkinson's group, who found me the most adorable, loving and I think perfect rescue dog, my life has improved so much with her joy. We both need each other, and it is nice to have an even relationship.

I am at that age that saying goodbye happens all too often. The difference is now I understand the pain and can offer to be a friend. When I am able to 'pay it forward,' it feels like a way to honour my adored husband, Bob.

I have no idea about tomorrow. I am still learning to want there to be a tomorrow. But I have also learned to count my blessings before I go to sleep and that brings me some comfort. I will never be the same person, but I still laugh, find joy, and remember how lucky I was to find such a great guy to spend 53 years with.

How Do You Feel?

What do you know about yourself now, that you didn't know before your loved one chose MAID?

JOYFUL

The things that your loved ones enjoyed are still with you. When you see something they would have loved, you can smile and acknowledge it, even reminisce about the times you were together. These joyous moments are to be cherished as testaments to the love you shared.

By embracing joy, you are uplifted and brought closer to your loved one, who you know is finally at peace.

Dave L. shares the joy he feels knowing his wife Annie is always with him.

Dave L.

It's moving into late summer. Under the Japanese maple that's just beginning to turn, birds peck at sunflower seeds in an old dish. A butterfly floats lazily over the grass. This was one of our favourite

Chapter 9

times of year, cool enough for Annie to be out in the sun, while also warm enough to spend time outside. Memories of our last day brush across my mind, bringing with them a sense of peace and joy. There is no grief, no sadness, no sense of loss.

I can feel her presence and allow my eyes to rest on the things she would have rested her eyes on. I feel her joy in each moment — the maple tree, the butterfly, the bright scarlet and blue parrots that are as common here as the pigeons back home. It's the end of February and I'm visiting a friend in the Blue Mountains of Australia. Tomorrow, this friend and I will begin another journey to see more friends and teach a meditation retreat in Taiping, Malaysia. Annie feels as light and as bright as a parrot's feather, no baggage to weigh her down. There's little need for conversation; she speaks to me most often through the voices of others, strange dreams they whisper to me, as if speaking them aloud might upset me. They speak an Annie sentence that takes them by surprise, or not. She has them taking care of me. Annie and I always planned to travel, and now we are free to flow from one moment to the next, from one place to another. Annie has her list, I have mine, and we don't argue.

Moving on from what? Life is a journey from one moment to the next. For me, it's a journey shared with Annie, as much now as it was before. Annie's body had become a burden that she was happy to set aside and without that baggage our journey together is much lighter.

Death for Annie was no Grim Reaper waiting in the shadows, but a gentle, patient soul that gave her the gift of time to close her life in the way she wanted and to give her a good and peaceful death. Annie has given me that gift of time and in whatever form my own death takes, I will be at peace.

How Do You Feel?
Explore your own feelings of joy after MAID.

LONGING

One of the many challenges facing those who have lost spouses is making the decision to seek out new love. There may be feelings of guilt. However, the longing to again welcome love into your life is natural and a testament to the infinite nature of love. You can never have too much love!

Dave B. shares how his longing for love following his wife's MAID led him to experience the extraordinary joy of again falling in love.

Dave B.

In the months after Annie died, I talked with as many friends as I could. Annie had a wide circle of friends, and I would unload to anyone who would listen. I just wanted to be heard and feel connection. Most of these friends started as Annie's friends — all women. She seemed to make life-long connections wherever she spent much time.

After many months, I became aware that I wanted to love again. To my mind, there is nothing more worthwhile in life. I will always love Annie. She will always be with me, in my mind and in my heart, but there's a difference between loving someone who is dead and someone who is alive. Loving someone who is no longer here is a bit one-sided. Loving the memories I created with Annie is not the same as loving another human being. I wanted to be with and love someone alive too; someone with passions to share and love to give. I wanted to feel alive.

Chapter 9

Annie had not wanted me to be alone. She used to tease me about having an affair with someone down at the supermarket, and even suggested a mutual friend of ours as someone I could possibly be with after she died. She always looked out for me, even as she was leaving me behind. I think she understood the importance of loving someone who is alive, before I did.

Ten months after Annie died, I did fall in love again, quite unexpectedly. I attended an art exhibit at a local gallery and was knocked out by the work of one of the artists, who happened to be staffing the show when I was there. Her work was different from Annie's, more intricate and three-dimensional, but the kind of thing that Annie would have loved. I asked her if she would write an article for a newsletter I edited. She did, and we met a few times, and then regularly.

We hiked together, we made meals together and watched movies together. I was smitten and it felt magical. I felt alive again as I emerged from my flat existence. I had forgotten what joy felt like, and now I was feeling it again.

How Do You Feel?

Have you felt a feeling of longing after your loved one's death? What or who do you long for?

FULFILLED

Supporting a loved one through MAID is an intense experience. Few models exist to show you how to deal with a planned death. You may never have thought much about death, seeing it more as something to ignore and deny.

Moving Forward

The MAID experience may lead you to question your beliefs about death. You've just supported someone who *chose* death — how do you go forward? For Robin and Nikki, finding fulfillment following their loved one's MAID came in the form of helping others.

Nikki

I'd started on this path as a daughter who was helping her father die. I felt as though I had fulfilled some sort of Karmic duty, almost like I had been chosen to be my father's daughter in order to help him through this chapter of his life. I felt fulfilled.

The one-year anniversary of my dad's death arrived, and I typed out the email I had memorised in my brain for over half a year. I wanted to know what I could do to help others who were going through or considering MAID. I wanted to take my experience and use it in a way that would help others navigate these dark and lonely waters.

I heard a calling to be a part of this death positive movement. I don't think I could or even would have ever imagined myself being where I am now. Being able to actively support those seeking MAID and those grieving a MAID loss eases my own pain and brings me joy and deep satisfaction that my own suffering was not in vain.

I feel proud and certain that I am making a difference in creating more of a narrative around death in our death-denying society. This, I believe, eases people's fear of death. I know that I am not as scared as I was once of what death means. I do not see it as a hard end. I see it as part of a chapter of our lives. Another milestone. One we should not fear as much as we do. It is the birth of whatever is next.

I am still in an active relationship with my father. Our relationship has continued to evolve even though he is not physically here. I had no idea that this was even possible — that there could be healing and that I would still converse with him and feel him and hear him come through. There are moments when I can feel his energy around me. And energy never dies.

My MAID experience has informed the way I now live. We do not have all the time in the world, so the time is now to do the things I've always wanted to do, to have the hard conversations with the ones I love and to not be so scared to get out there and just be me and go for what I want. And, for me, that is a life that feels much richer and more alive than I can remember it feeling pre-MAID.

Robin

I strongly believe in MAID and that people should have a choice to end their life with support when appropriate. But a MAID patient is just one person among many in a network touched by that decision, and the people left behind have a lot to grapple with.

When my dad died, I found some relief in a Facebook group for people touched by MAID, which helped immensely in the days after. From there, I found another organization that provides peer support to people who are either supporting someone or grieving someone through MAID, and I contacted them about joining.

I had decided shortly after my dad died that I wanted to do something about the huge gap in support for people going through this. It just didn't feel right that there was nowhere to turn for help or answers to basic questions, and I figured I could help do something about it. I've done this before after personal struggles and have found it really gratifying. When I first started offering peer support to people with a loved one choosing MAID, it felt to me like things in the world were balancing out a little bit: I hadn't had any support, but now I was helping to make sure others did. And then I had an opportunity to get more involved in the running of the organization.

I have a friend who talks about the importance of alignment between yourself and the things you do and between yourself and the people you surround yourself with. I definitely know what it feels like when those things don't line up, when we don't have something meaningful in our lives or we lack people who care about the same things we do. I hadn't been looking for that when I started volunteering; I just wanted to help people. But, quite unexpectedly, I found that doing this type of work filled me up in other ways. I found people who appreciated what I had to offer. They not only understood my experience, but they gave me a space to turn it into something meaningful.

The people I volunteer with really care about helping people through one of the darkest times in their lives and doing it with compassion. And on top of that, they are some of the kindest, wisest, and most generous people I've ever known. Working alongside them to do something that really makes a difference has been a delight in ways I couldn't have anticipated.

My dad's MAID death was one day, but I've chosen to make something of it that has brought joy to me in all the days after.

How Do You Feel?
Has your experience with MAID led you to a place of fulfillment? Do you want it to?

Chapter 9

FREE

If you've been a caretaker for a long time prior to your loved one's MAID, your grief may well be mixed with a newfound sense of freedom. You're suddenly able to do things you weren't able to before, and while you may experience a certain amount of fear of the unknown, you might also feel exhilarated and excited. You've been given an opportunity to re-create yourself, to do some of the things you've never had a chance to do in your life, and to go forward into your new life with a renewed sense of wonder.

Geneviève and Jane share how they felt empowered by the freedom they experienced following the deaths of their spouses.

Geneviève

Having to figure things out on my own, in this new life without my partner, has been incredibly challenging but also very rewarding and empowering. It has given me the opportunity to discover myself and understand myself better. I'm learning what is important to me and how I want to live my life. I don't have it all figured out, but I am less afraid and reluctant to try things now. I feel myself becoming my own person.

I've learned to rely on myself. For example, Duncan used to do all the chainsaw jobs in the yard. I'm sure he would have been a lumberjack in another life. When the branches needed pruning and clearing for a new fence to be put in, I took the bull by the horns, bought myself a dual hedger and a chainsaw and went at it. Funny thing, I loved every minute of it. Once that first branch came down, there was no stopping me. I ended up talking to Duncan and telling him that now I understood why he liked doing it so much. I cleared more than I needed to and put it all beside the house for sorting and chopping into wood for the winter. I felt amazing.

Duncan and I did some travelling together, but I wasn't sure how that part of my life was going to look after he was gone. Not everyone wants to do the trips I want to do. I didn't want to travel on my own, but I also didn't want to give up something I had always enjoyed. So, I didn't! I found a company that does tours for women, and I booked myself a trip to Tanzania. It was one of the most freeing things I have ever done. I came home feeling more confident and determined to do more things.

These small achievements helped me gain a better footing and they empowered me to be active in my life. I've become clearer about the life I want to lead and who I want in it. Most importantly, it's helped give meaning to the life Duncan and I built together.

I know how I want to move forward from here. All of my experiences have shaped the person I will be in the future. I am becoming her.

Jane

It was understood that after my husband completed MAID that I would move out west to be with my family. The thought of fixing the house, selling, packing and actually starting a new life in a new province was daunting and scary, but also kind of exciting. It was actually quite freeing. As much as I loved my husband, the years of caretaking stress and exhaustion had taken their toll on me. I felt relieved to be free from that.

I was suddenly free to make choices strictly for myself, to be true to myself. I felt like a kid again, delighted to try so many things I had not been able to do before. It was like a veil had been lifted from my eyes and a fog dissipated from my brain. I was no longer a caretaker, which had been my only purpose for so long, and now the possibilities seemed endless. I felt excited to reinvent myself, and it was powerful!

Chapter 9

At first, I was overwhelmed with this freedom. I didn't know where to begin. I decided to start with selling my house, which gave me a new purpose and brightened my outlook on life.

I wanted to be thoughtful about the major decisions that were before me because I recognized that this newfound freedom also came with responsibility. This made me feel powerful. It wasn't the ego kind of power, but the power of control I had over my life and choosing what kind of life I wanted to lead now that I was only responsible for myself. It was so exhilarating that at times I felt light-headed with new ideas and possibilities. I had to step back a little and catch my breath. Courage is a feeling I didn't think much about at the time but in the end, it did take courage to embrace the freedom of my new life.

How Do You Feel?

Explore the moments you have felt free since your loved one had MAID.

GRATEFUL

You expect that grief takes time and that sadness will last forever, and we can be scared to ask ourselves if we will ever be happy again. We wonder if it's okay to want to be happy again.

One day you might take a look around and realize that the life you are living does make you happy. You may even realize that you are grateful for the experience and what it's taught you.

Cynthia shares her feelings of gratitude for being able to talk about her love for her husband with her new love.

Moving Forward

Cynthia

My family and I spend a lot of time in the mountains; walking our dog, skiing in the Rockies, and hiking to views that make our existence feel small and insignificant. One day in particular, we were on a trail covered in scree, with a rather steep drop to one side. I listened to a conversation between my child and my boyfriend as we continued along the trail, which felt as big as I felt small in that moment.

"My daddy would have hated this."

"Really, why is that?"

"My daddy was scared of heights."

"Huh, I didn't know that."

"He would have loved all these rocks though. He studied rocks."

"He sounds like he was a pretty cool guy."

"Yeah, he was. I wish you could have met him."

My heart swells and I catch a tear forming in my eye. I feel overwhelmed with gratitude to be in the most beautiful place on earth with the three people I love most, talking about the one who is missing. I have happy kids who feel comfortable talking about their dead dad and a boyfriend who doesn't make it weird. We frequently joke about the things my husband used to say or do, and the ways he would drive me crazy. I point out the similarities between him and my kids, and my boyfriend sometimes even joins in. I feel fortunate to have a boyfriend who loves us and doesn't try to compete with the memory of my late husband.

My biggest fear was that losing their father would 'ruin' my children, but it hasn't. The truth is that it has made us all more empathetic, compassionate and open to the dichotomies in life. I am so grateful that my children know they are loved by two fathers—one who is dead, but who left them an unshakeable foundation of pride and affection, and one who is here every day learning new lessons with them and going on adventures to new heights.

If someone had told me three and half years ago that I would feel happy again, and grateful to be living a wonderful life again, I probably would have slapped them and cried. But here we are. We ARE living a beautiful life, and we are thriving. It's nothing like the life I had pictured; watching our children grow-up and growing old with my husband, but we are happy, and it feels right.

My children learned young that life is not fair, that grief does not end, but that happiness still exists in the shadows. I'm grateful every day that they know it's okay to feel sad and happy at the same time, and that love is not finite.

I too wish my boyfriend could have met my husband.

How Do You Feel?
Do you feel grateful for having had this MAID experience?

WHAT'S YOUR STORY?

Moving forward after your loved one's death is challenging, but ultimately, it's something we all need to do. *How* we move forward differs from person to person, the commonality being that everyone is still on a journey that will be a part of them for the rest of their lives. How did you move forward after your loved one's death?

Listed below are each of the emotions presented as our storytellers found ways to move forward.

- Proud
- Sadness
- Incomplete
- Peaceful
- Purposeful
- Inspired

- Self-Aware
- Joyful
- Longing
- Fulfilled
- Free
- Grateful

How Do You Feel?

Which emotions and stories resonate with you?

Which emotions do not resonate with you?

What emotions did you feel, that were not included?

Has anything that you've felt during your journey surprised you?

CONCLUSION

In *The Many Faces of MAID*, our storytellers have shared a myriad of ways they have reacted, felt and supported themselves and their loved ones through a Medically Assisted Death. No emotions were off the table — from anger to confusion to gratitude to love, encompassing the good, the bad, the expected, and the unexpected.

As storytellers, we have shared some of our toughest moments, hardest feelings and most unexpected or surprising emotions, in the hopes that anyone struggling through this experience will find validation and companionship. You truly are not alone.

Your MAID journey will not be like anyone else's, but we hope you find moments of connection. Use this book as your support and your guide. We have learned so much compiling the stories in this book and trust you will too.

Cynthia Clark & Carol Cram

INDEX OF EMOTIONS

Conclusion

RESOURCES

Use the following resources to help you find support for your own MAID journey or for the journey of someone in your life who needs help.

Eligibility Information

- https://www.canada.ca/en/health-canada/services/health-services-benefits/medical-assistance-dying.html
- https://camapcanada.ca/for-the-public/eligibility/
- https://www.dyingwithdignity.ca/end-of-life-support/navigating-a-request-for-medical-assistance-in-dying/

National Organizations

- **MAID Family Support Society (MFSS)**
  www.maidfamilysupport.ca info@maidfamilysupport.ca, One-to-one peer support both before and after a MAID death. Formerly known as Bridge4You.
- **Canadian Association of MAID Assessors and Providers**
  https://camapcanada.ca/
- **Dying With Dignity Canada**
  https://www.dyingwithdignity.ca/
  support@dyingwithdignity.ca
  National Office: 416-486-3998

Resources

- **MAiDHouse**
  https://www.maidhouse.ca/
- **Bridge C-14**
  www.bridgec14.org Web-based group peer support for individuals choosing MAID and loved ones who have experienced a MAID loss.
- **Canada Virtual Hospice**
  www.virtualhospice.ca Educational resource for end of life, grief, and MAID.

Provincial Resources

Alberta

- **Alberta Health Services**: www.ahs.ca/maid
- **MAID Care Team**: Maid.CareTeam@ahs.ca or 811
- **AHS Bob Glasgow Grief Support Centre**: 403-955-8444 individual and group bereavement counselling
- **Children's Grief Centre Calgary**: 403-263-4525 Email: info@childrensgriefcentre.ca www.hospicecalgary.ca
- **Hospice**: www.hospicecalgary.ca 403-263-4525
- **Geriatric Mental Health**: Sheldon Shumir Clinic: 403-955-6155

British Columbia

- **General information**
  https://www2.gov.bc.ca/gov/content/health/accessing-health-care/home-community-care/care-options-and-cost/end-of-life-care/medical-assistance-in-dying
- **Fraser Health Authority**
  Phone: 604-587-7878
  Email: mccc@fraserhealth.ca
  https://www.fraserhealth.ca/health-topics-a-to-z/end-of-life-care/medical-assistance-in-dying

Resources

- **Vancouver Coastal Health MAID**
  Phone: 1-844-550-5556 or 604-875-4249 (outside of BC)
  Email: assisteddying@vch.ca
  https://www.vch.ca/en/service/medical-assistance-dying
- **Vancouver Island**: Phone: 250-727-4382 (Greater Victoria)
  Phone Toll-Free: 1-877-370-8699
  Email: maid@islandhealth.ca
  https://www.islandhealth.ca/learn-about-health/medical-assistance-dying/medical-assistance-dying
- **Northern Health**: Phone: 250-645-8549
  Email: maid@northernhealth.ca
  https://www.northernhealth.ca/health-topics/medical-assistance-dying-maid
- **Interior Health**: Phone: 250-469-7073 (Kelowna area)
  Phone Toll-Free: 1-844-469-7073
  Email: maid@interiorhealth.ca
  https://www.interiorhealth.ca/health-and-wellness/palliative-and-end-of-life-care/medical-assistance-in-dying

Manitoba
- **Manitoba MAID team**: Phone: (204) 926-1380
  Email: maid@sharedhealthmb.ca
  https://www.gov.mb.ca/health/maid.html

- **Palliative Manitoba**: Phone: (204) 889-8525
  www.palliativemanitoba.ca

New Brunswick
- **Government of New Brunswick Health Medical Assistance in Dying**:
  https://www2.gnb.ca/content/gnb/en/departments/health/patientinformation/content/MedicalAssistanceInDying.html

Resources

- **Horizon Health Network MAID Information**:
  Phone Toll-Free 1-833-8836243 or 811
  MAID@horizonNB.ca; https://horizonnb.ca/patients-visitors/patient-information-resources/medical-assistance-in-dying-maid/
- **Vitality Health Network**: Call 811 or
  Phone: 1-877-286-1311
  Email: qualite.quality@vitalitenb.ca
  https://www.vitalitenb.ca/en/patients/end-life-care/medical-assistance-dying

Newfoundland & Labrador
- **Provincial Information and FAQs**:
  https://www.gov.nl.ca/hcs/files/faq-pdf-medical-assistance-dying.pdf
- **Central Health**: Phone: 709-235-1412
  Email: maid@centralhealth.nl.ca
  https://www.centralhealth.nl.ca/medical-assistance-in-dying
- **Eastern Health**: Phone: 709-777-2250
  Toll-Free: 833-777-2250
  Email: maid@easternhealth.ca
- **Labrador-Grenfell Health**: Phone: 709-454-0665
  Email: maid@lghealth.ca
- **Western Health**: Phone: 709-784-2804
  Email: maid@westernhealth.nl.ca

Northwest Territories
- **Health and Social Services MAID Information**:
  Phone Toll-Free: 1-833-492-0131
  Email: maid_careteam@gov.nt.ca
  https://www.hss.gov.nt.ca/en/services/medical-assistance-dying-maid

Resources

Nova Scotia

- **Nova Scotia Health Authority MAID Information**: Phone: 902-491-5892 or 1-833-903-6243 toll free
  Email: maid@nshealth.ca
  https://www.nshealth.ca/maid
  https://www.nshealth.ca/patient-education-resources/2229

Nunavut

- **Nunavut Department of Health**:
  Email: maid.info@gov.nu.ca
  Phone: 867-975-5700

Ontario

- **Ontario Government MAID Information**: **Care Coordination Service**: Phone Toll-Free: 1-866-286-4023
  TTY: 1-844-953-3350
  https://www.ontario.ca/page/medical-assistance-dying-and-end-life-decisions
- **MAiDHouse**: https://www.maidhouse.ca/

Prince Edward Island

- **Prince Edward Island MAID Information**:
  Phone: 902-288-1096
  Email: HPEIProvSpecialtyVC@ihis.org
  https://www.princeedwardisland.ca/en/information/health-pei/medical-assistance-in-dying

Quebec

- **MAID Information**: Phone Toll-Free: 877-644-4545
  Montreal: 514-644-4545
  Quebec City: 418-644-4545
  Or call 811 for more information
  https://www.quebec.ca/en/health/health-system-and-services/end-of-life-care/medical-aid-in-dying/

Resources

- Medical assistance in dying (in French):
  Toll Free: 877-644-4545
  Montreal: 514-644-4545
  Quebec: 418-644-4545
  Call Info-Santé (811) for more information;
  https://www.quebec.ca/sante/health-system-and-services/end-of-life-care/medical-aid-to-die/

Saskatchewan

- **Saskatchewan Health Authority MAID Information**:
  Phone: 833-473-6243 or 306-766-4399 or 811
  Email: provincialmaidprogram@saskhealthauthority.ca
  https://www.saskhealthauthority.ca/your-health/conditions-diseases-services/all-z/medical-assistance-dying/accessing-maid-saskatchewan

Yukon

- **Yukon Health and Social Services MAID Information**:
  Phone: 867-667-5695
  Phone Toll-Free: 1-800-661-0408 ext. 5695
  Email: hss@gov.yk.ca; https://yukon.ca/en/health-and-wellness/find-information-about-medical-assistance-dying

ACKNOWLEDGEMENTS

We would like to thank all the people who supported us during the writing of *The Many Faces of MAID*.

Our Storytellers

First and most importantly are the 15 individuals who agreed to share their MAID stories by meeting with us over the course of nine months. Thank you for your candour and your courage.

Carole Atkinson, Jane Piercy-Ballard, Dave Byrnes, Daimhin Chinnery, Elizabeth Ethier, Robin Farr, Nikki Gouzopoulos, Shannon Knight, Dave Leggatt, Geneviève McLean, Andrée Morel, Bobbie Putman, Cathy Skeen, Emily Wilson, and Brittney Wright

Our Reviewers

We would also like to thank the many people in the MAID community who gave us feedback about *The Many Faces of MAID*.

Dr. Stefanie Green, author of *This is Assisted Dying*, met with us and encouraged us when we were beginning this project and provided feedback on the completed book. Signy Novak, founder of the MAID Family Support Society that published this book, wrote the foreword to this book and also provided many valuable insights. Lauren Clark of Bridge C-14 introduced us and encouraged us to work together to write the book.

Acknowledgements

Other people who reviewed the book and provided much-appreciated feedback include:

- Tekla Hendrickson, Executive Director of MAiDHouse
- Katherine Cortes-Miller, Associate Professor, School of Social Work Director, Centre for Education and Research on Aging & Health (CERAH) Lakehead University
- Keri-Lynn Durant, BEd, PhD, Heartsteps Centre for Grief Literacy, Co-Host of the *Disrupting Death Podcast*
- June Churchill, Kerrie Hale, Kelsey Goforth and Sarah Dobec from Dying with Dignity
- Diana Steele, Cory Steinke, Mari Dekker, Marilyn Clark, Kim McClean, and Sheryl Williamson.

Thank you also to Cathy Skeen and Dave Byrnes who proofread the book, and to John Dowler for designing the cover and Gregg Simpson for providing the cover art.

Cynthia would also like to thank Tyler for his constant support, willingness to listen and learn, and for embracing the chaos of being someone's chapter two.

Carol would also like to thank her husband Gregg and daughter Julia for their constant, heartfelt support, and her best friend Stephanie Williams who is always willing to listen and help.

ABOUT THE AUTHORS

Cynthia Clark guided her family through MAID in 2019 when her husband was diagnosed with brain cancer. It has become her mission to normalize talking about death and dying, especially with children. Cynthia received her HBA from the University of Western Ontario and lived and worked in several different countries with her late husband. She is a trained executive coach and seasoned advocate for many causes that she is passionate about. She is a volunteer for her local Dying with Dignity chapter and a board member with MAID Family Support Society. In her free time, Cynthia enjoys cross country skiing, mountain biking, writing, puzzles and watching her kids play sports.

Carol Cram is the author of four novels, along with several dozen textbooks on computer applications and communications. She was on faculty at Capilano University in North Vancouver for over two decades and holds an MA in Drama and an MBA. In 2021, she supported her mother through MAID and was inspired by the experience to co-author this book. Carol lives with her husband, artist Gregg Simpson, on Bowen Island in BC. She loves reading, dancing Nia, and traveling every chance she gets.

Made in United States
North Haven, CT
28 March 2024

50617455R00157